this
one
has
no
name.

this one has no name.

the no name
writing group

Published by Spuyten Duyvil
An imprint of Hobo Jungle Press
Sharon, Connecticut, USA
St. Vincent & the Grenadines

First edition
Printed in the United States of America

ISBN #978-0-9829945-9-7
Library of Congress Control Number: 2016954402

Cover design by Joe Connolly

Dedication

This anthology is dedicated to Fran and Michael Keilty,
owners of The Hickory Stick Bookshop
in Washington, Connecticut.
They provide the no name writing group
a haven where we meet, give readings, buy books,
and gather for conversation;
a place where we build and share our stories.
We are grateful to them for their kindness,
faith and generosity all these years.

Contents

Introduction

A friend of mine told me that meaningful culture is passed along in small settings. Narrative and poetry reflect this. Intimate acts require a speaker and an active listener/reader. Telling and hearing stories and poems are what make us human. They help give shape to our experience. In giving voice to ideas and emotions through images and language, writers hope to better understand the world and themselves. Writers offer a way of seeing and feeling that is both uniquely contemporary but also speaks to the timeless soul of the human condition.

The no name writers group has a rich, decades-long history in the literary life of Washington, Connecticut. Contributing poet Davyne Verstandig explained, "Over 30 years ago I was invited to the home of Susan Tidyman (her husband was the author of *The French Connection*). Each year she gave a party to celebrate Edna St. Vincent Millay's birthday. Susan invited a number of women to the party and a man — Robley Whitson. She sent Edna's sister Nora a bouquet of flowers and called her on the phone. Then we all ate and drank and read some of our poems. Nan Malone, one of the early members was also at that celebration. A few days later Robley mentioned that it was too bad we'd have to wait another year to get together and read what we wrote. We decided to start meeting at the Hickory Stick Bookshop with a few friends, and so it began."

Comprised of an eclectic mix of poets, novelists, short story writers, performers, essayists, and visual artists, the configuration of the group has shifted gradually over time, with meetings held in a variety of settings. In spite of this seemingly amorphous identity, the writers are a firmly established presence in Connecticut's northwest hills where they frequently stage readings, perform in coffee houses, or partner in artistic collaborations.

The group decided not to label itself beyond the No-Name Writers Group. They preferred the breadth of their writing to create the group's identity.

Despite its inconspicuous name, the group's mission remains driven by its vitality of ideas.

The members of the No Name Writers Group have come together in different ways and for different reasons. Like many of the contributors to this volume, Merima Trako, who describes herself on her website as a mom, engineer, ex-refugee, writer, has found a home in the group.

"I am here, meeting with people, like me, who have stories to share. They want to be heard," Merima said. "Our collective writing is an echo of the souls that need companionship, an affirmation, that we matter, that somehow our writing talents are not alone and hidden under our 'real lives'. All of us are stuck in this duality, this existence that transforms what our 'normal selves' are, to something that our deepest truths want to reveal. In this group of writers I feel that I found soul mates for the part of me that never quits writing. We create our own identity through companionship, laughter and appreciation for each other's work."

Nan Adams, a No Name Writer who has since passed away, wrote in the introduction to the group's 2010 anthology, *Songs of the Marrow Bone,* "The group has convened in a town hall, committee room, in the lobby of a real estate office, and in various people's houses." They've also met at The Pantry, a local restaurant. Currently they meet at the Hickory Stick Book Shop in Washington Depot, where owners Fran and Michael Keilty graciously offer the store after hours.

The culmination of the last year's writing and meetings is reflected in the prose and poetry they've selected for *This One Has No Name.* It is my hope this book will introduce readers to the rich and varied voices grounded in community. Through the power of their work, I hope you will be able to identify with them and with some part of yourself you might not have known existed.

This introduction has been a collaborative effort, reflecting the way we respect and honor one another's ideas.

Tom Lagasse
2016

1

Alice Barstow

Confessions

When I broke away from Melody, I knew I couldn't escape the stinging feeling of being left out. That's what scared me the most when I began to distance myself — not only from her - but from the entire group. All of these ladies I had collected since my first days of being a mom — of moving to the rural suburbs to start a new life with my family.

I met Julia at a play group for mothers — Melody and Alexis during story time at a local bookstore. The others were just always in my mommy vision. As our kids graduated preschool — getting into the elementary years — we moms were reaching middle age — and things got fun.

Suddenly there we were — passing out shots of whiskey at a bar instead of picking up each other's pacifiers on the playground. No one was working full time yet. There were a lot of weekday nights out drinking — and early morning hangovers as I shuffled the kids onto the bus. I knew the party had to end.

I think it became real for me around the third time I collapsed into my bed and had to resort to my old college trick of placing one foot on the floor to stop the walls from spinning around me. I said it quietly to myself one morning — while standing at the kitchen sink, "I can't keep up." And I knew what that meant — standing apart — standing alone. Soon, I was going to feel lonely.

I recently came across a picture of me, Melody, Julia and a few others, arm in arm, before the burlesque show in Boston. We all prettied up in lipstick and sexy black tops, sipping oversized martinis at the burlesque bar — a small narrow space tucked in the warm mahogany room lit up by a crystal ball casting diamonds. "That's the night it all turned ugly," Lincoln said as he noticed me staring at the picture.

I don't know how it happened or even why, but as the opening act exited the stage, Julia, who was sitting next to me at the small round table, leaned in close, looked straight into my eyes and quietly confessed that she was sleeping with her neighbor's husband — her neighbor, who was sitting at the same table just a few seats away. I didn't even have time to think or respond before the red velvety stage curtains went up and our first act appeared. A beautiful milky white dancer sat prettily atop a swinging bar from center stage, adorning a tattered Tinker Bell costume with exposed breasts and jeweled nipples complete with green tasseled pasties. With pointed toes, our dancer slowly kicked her legs, a sultry swing to and fro, all the while wearing a smirk that said she held a secret we all wanted to know.

For the next few months, Julia would visit my kitchen table as I fed her tea and my ear while she confessed her digressions in gritty detail. It weighed heavy on my heart. She talked of the cheating — the threesomes — the fucking of someone else's husband in the upstairs bathroom while the kids ate pizza and watched Harry Potter downstairs — as if this cast of characters weren't the moms and dads I saw every day — at school and on the soccer field — as if I didn't know their children who were in the same class as my own. I couldn't stop her from telling me. And a part of me couldn't stop from wanting to know.

Shame

The sound of "mommeeee" feels like a knife stabbing me in the eye. I'm trying to be patient — remembering how Rose is this whiney and needy only because she had a total of three hours of sleep last night — which equals the exact amount I had. We haven't had a night this bad since Rose was first diagnosed, at ten months old, with juvenile rheumatoid arthritis. But then, she was just a baby, whining and crying like babies do at night. Now, at four, she's a little girl — rubbing her hands, crying in pain, stretching her limbs — trying to rid herself of the deep ache she feels.

Usually she whimpers and stirs in her sleep — rolling about our bed until she snuggles her tiny round head between my breasts, taking her small hand and rubbing it up and down, up and down, on the upper portion of my left arm — a habit she acquired the day she discovered she could move her arms at all. It started while nursing. She would look up at me with her hazel brown eyes, her pudgy little fingers rub, rub, rubbing my arm, every now and again pausing to give me a tight little squeeze. In the winter months, she'd muscle her hand up my shirt sleeve until she found skin. And now, as she continues this skin to skin mantra, I quietly pat her back, a substitute for the nursing that has since ceased. I will pat, pat, pat — until I feel her body relax, somehow untangling from its familiar chronic ache, to finally fall back into sleep.

But last night her pain struck with a much mightier force. She slept for only an hour before she rose with a cry and then came stumbling out of her bedroom toward me and Michael sitting on the couch. Her little face was scrunched up and angry. I cradled her in my arms, held her head close to my chest, and tried humming and rocking her, but she couldn't sit still. She just kept whimpering and kicking her legs, stretching her arms toward my chest, looking up at me as if to say, "Why have you done this to me — and why won't you make it stop?"

One of the first things I said to the rheumatologist after Rose's diagnosis was, "I don't understand how this happened. I'm a nursing mother." It was a raw emotion — that came from a place within me that foolishly believed my breast milk really was powerful enough to fend off such disease. Why else would I suffer breasts that felt and looked like two boulders atop my chest — the cracked, infected nipples — and then the thrush and clogged ducts? Why else did I commit so fiercely to feed my child from myself, from my own body, if I didn't somehow think it was a miracle food?

The doctor looked at me confusingly and simply said, "This is in no way your fault, you did nothing to make this happen." I've heard versions of this sentiment from nurses, pediatricians and physical therapists, over the years. But as any decent mom knows — our guilt is not made of sound logic. It's just a gut feeling — a natural intuition that goes back to the time of Eve biting that fucking apple — that all *is* our fault. And I am no fool. I can see the look in the other moms' eyes — hear the little voice in their heads — trying to sum up what I did wrong to make this happen and how they can avoid such a fate. Some not so subtle moms will blurt out questions like, "So, how did Rose get this — did she get it from you...?" That was a fun play date. Because you see, the *blame* is also as natural and illogical as the guilt.

And the answer is yes, of course I think she got it from me. Rose is from my gene pool. She looks and acts just like me — unlike my six-year old Grace, who came out with her father's head attached to her body. And just like my husband, Grace is quiet, reserved, neat, and analytical. Rose, like me, stumbles about the house clumsily, leaving trails of messes and play behind her — talk, talk, talking all the while. So yes, my gene pool, of having relatives with other auto-immune disorders — my defected, mistake of a gene — infected my baby girl. I must have known this, on some subconscious level, for the moment I knew I was having another girl, I named her Rose. I didn't do this with Grace. With Grace, Michael and I flipped through a dozen baby name books, wrote different versions of different names in notebooks and on paper napkins at restaurants. We finally settled on two choices — Chloe or Grace. We agreed to make a final decision on her birthday, when we would finally meet her in person.

Grace arrived peaceful and quiet. She was calm and still as she curled up in my arms, her large almond-shaped eyes so serious and serene. We knew immediately that she was our *Grace*. But with Rose, I hardly opened up one name book. My grandmother once asked me when I was still pregnant, "Why Rose?" She said the name as if it didn't settle right on her tongue, and I could tell she wasn't happy.

"I don't know" I said, "I have just always loved the name." I wasn't sure why I liked the name so much, and always believed the name called to me, and this little soul inside me, more than I called to it. I now know this feeling to be bitterly accurate, because *Rose* is, as the flower, so very strong and beautiful, yet fragile and vulnerable to disease.

"Roses are so hard to grow and take care of," I recently overheard a woman in the grocery store checkout tell the cashier, "they're so susceptible to disease". And my heart panged at these words. I felt sick to my stomach. "It is my fault," I thought, "I should have never named her Rose."

Roses are hard to grow. They are vulnerable. They are hard to keep healthy. They require work, care, medicine, love, and appreciation. And today, as I hear my Rose moan from the vulnerable opening of her soul, "mommeeee" — my very tired self realizes that to grow *my* Rose takes a strength and perseverance that most days, I don't believe I have. Because you see, in my own garden, I don't bother trying to grow roses.

9

C. E. Wyllie

Greenleaf "Hunter"Davis
Photo courtesy of Lore Rogers,
Patten Lumberman's Museum, Patten, Maine

The Hermit of Shin Pond

Alice Louise Leslie listened intently. Was it the lake breeze that she heard? Or was it the distant, mournful sound of Hunter Davis, Shin Pond's strange hermit? Sitting on the rock in front of Mr. Moody's family camp, she concentrated again, straining her ears, scrunching up her face involuntarily, as she tried to filter out the background cacophony of early summer evenings in northern Maine. Peepers and crickets harmonized with an occasional loon or owl. Bats fluttered down upon the glassy surface of the water, reflecting the faded plum of twilight, silhouetted by the jagged outline of spruce, white pine, and the dominant arch of Mt. Chase. *Serenade me, Mr. Greenleaf.* She let out her breath with a wistful romanticism that seemed to awaken in her just as the mud and black flies were disappearing, and summer's promise more than a taunt.

Inside the camp her father, Ilber Leslie, was conversing with Mr. Moody and a visitor from Boston, Mr. George Callendar Reed. Alice diverted herself from thinking about their conversation — a conversation she imagined taking place at this very moment. Mr. Reed had certainly alluded to his intentions. Such intentions pressed against her like impending autumn heralding the inescapable frost of seemingly endless winters in the Katahdin woods. For the present, it was summer. She closed her eyes, as though in doing so she could will Hunter's bow to descend across the strings of his handmade fiddle.

As a child, she had been afraid of Greenleaf "Hunter" Davis. She remembered how the old man had seemed fixated on her long, curly blond tresses with such a strange, haunted look on his face. He had touched them once, with that oddly distant and trace-like gaze. She had pulled away abruptly. She hadn't liked it at all.

Now that she was in her twenties, Alice couldn't imagine why she had ever found the short, wiry man in the least bit frightening. Certainly he was intense; but it was that very intensity on topics shared in her company that gave her the courage to imagine the world differently, to question the commonplace around her in a way that would not have been possible in the remote village life of northern Penobscot, had she never made his acquaintance.

Mr. Davis was a hermit, but he was not a recluse. He emerged from his forest sanctuary on occasion with an outburst of opinions, cracking through the conservative town of Patten like unexpected thunder. Alice admired this quality for she, too, was opinionated; although this quality didn't often sit well with people — gentlemen in particular.

Mr. Davis could also be quiet and withdrawn in the company of others, but the mere sight of Alice drew the man out of his shell. He had introduced her to the fine literary company of Tennyson, Byron, Whittier, Thomas Campbell, and his favorite, Thomas Moore; companions, albeit on the printed page, far more interesting than the women of the Methodist Church quilting group and their infernal talk about babies.

She knew that the town women pitied her, because she didn't yet have a husband or even a fiancé, and she was already getting on in years. She didn't feel old. She was mystified that, trapped as these women seemed with their mindless chores and subservient roles, they should wish to promote such shared fates (although she never would have dared to say as much). She had no desire to be loved for her cooking (although she did make extraordinary brown bread and bean hole beans and everyone raved about them), nor for her way with children. She was one of the better teachers at Patten Academy, but she was always thankful that she needn't bring the young ones home. The repetitive responsibilities of domestic life bored her and Alice discovered, as she got older, that perhaps she was not always conscientious about giving her full attentions to such matters. Instead, she would sit at the piano in her parents' parlor, or journey on a beloved passage of verse:

How many loved your moments of glad grace,
And loved your beauty with love false or true,
But one man loved the pilgrim soul in you,
And loved the sorrows of your changing face.

They were the words of a contemporary poet, William Butler Yeats, but they expressed how she, too, wanted to be loved — for her pilgrim soul. The soul that longed to travel to Boston, New York, Europe, "or even India," she said, not realizing that she had uttered the words aloud.

A man like Mr. Davis could certainly appreciate that in a woman. It was too bad that he was an unkempt old hermit, for his ideas were daring, forthright and fine.

The smile on her lips betrayed her inner thoughts. He was extremely outspoken, in fact, on the subject of suffrage for women. And not only on the right to vote, but all manner of equal rights. He debated this point at a number of public meetings, and had written extensive editorials on the subject for the Bangor paper. The local men dismissed Hunter Davis as queer; but most men, Alice thought, hated the idea of women thinking.

Fireflies shimmered and pulsed like fireworks as the sky grew darker. People probably thought her queer, too, she imagined. She pondered the rumors that she had heard of Greenleaf Davis's earlier life, before he had arrived at the far end of Shin Pond.

The people of Patten loved to gossip. And while Alice tried to ignore this idle talk most of the time, she was extremely curious about Mr. Davis, who spoke very little about his early life, for he was an extremely private man.

Once, when the subject of Henry David Thoreau had come up, Hunter Davis had become extremely agitated. She had been sitting on Mr. Moody's screened-in porch after shared family dinner, when Hunter Davis chanced to pass by in his dugout canoe.

"Come and visit for a spell," Mr. Moody hollered to the old man.

Alice had loved reading Walden and Mr. Thoreau's essays; and when she had expressed this to the group, now congregated on the porch, Davis said that Thoreau was "an ungrateful, phony flatlander." His face twitched nervously, as it often did.

"When I was twenty-six, I guided for Thoreau in these woods. I took him part way up Katahdin, but he wasn't a very fit man. Then, years later, he wrote about his experiences in the Maine Woods and talked about having some Indian guide. He had no Indian guide! I was his guide and he didn't give me one bit of credit. They used to call me Pamola in those days. Pamola, like the summit of Katahdin."

Then he looked around at his small audience. "You don't believe me. I can see that."

The next time she saw Mr. Davis, he brought along a copy of the Bangor newspaper that he had borrowed from the Patten Town Library; a yellowed issue from 1843. It verified that Greenleaf Davis had accompanied Mr. Henry David Thoreau for several weeks in the Katahdin Woods.

Hunter Davis's skill as a woodsman was renowned. A self-sufficient naturalist, he made his living trapping beaver, although he hunted all manner of game, including bear (of which he had slain more than four hundred). Alice often saw him fishing in the lake from his canoe. When she visited the hermit's cabin with her father, she was delighted to see a fox appear out of the woods, who took food directly from Mr. Davis' hand.

Alice knew that Hunter Davis was originally from Lincoln, Maine. There was a somewhat tragically romantic tale associated with his younger years about which he steadfastly refused to talk. This shroud of mystery seemed to amplify an aura of star-crossed love, accentuated by the strains of the bow sliding across his beloved fiddle on evenings such as these.

She had never broached the subject of his past. Yet, the village folk relayed a series of stories connected with the fatal circumstances that had driven the old man away from his family. These stories, which Mr. Davis neither supported nor denied, were told with a frequency that rendered them real; though whether truth or fiction, Alice had no way of knowing. Something, however, she was certain, had forced Hunter Davis to live apart from other men. Something had created the enigma and complexities mirrored in his brooding eyes, the periodic bursts of passion.

And so the stories went, that when he was a youth, Greenleaf Davis's family had taken in a young girl. She was apparently of no relation, and while never legally adopted, had been looked upon as a daughter to the family. Greenleaf and this golden-haired girl were thrown together constantly, and thus came to fall deeply in love. When they went to his parents, wanting to marry, the elder Mr. Davis forbade it.

Greenleaf and the girl could not imagine a life without one another. Despite his father's objection to their marriage, they pledged their undying love, vowing to find a way to be together eternally. This portion of the story, the pledge of undying and eternal love, Alice was obliged to confess, was her own augmentation. For wasn't this the fate of all of history's great lovers: Romeo and Juliet, Pellees and Melisande, Tristan and Isolde, to be so tragically destined?

Some said his father might have reconsidered had Greenleaf been better able to support the girl. But were there other circumstances influencing his vehement objections, Alice wondered? Dark secrets casting an ominous shadow over the family, like ancient tales of Sophocles?

Whatever his motivations, it was said that in 1849, leaving his sweetheart behind, Greenleaf Davis left Maine to seek his fortune in the California gold rush. He wrote to her constantly ("I must hear from thee every day i'the hour, For in a minute there are many days: Of by this count I shall be much in years...") and with great enthusiasm of his successes in amassing wealth. And although dismayed when his letters received no reply, he never lost faith. Nine years later, fortune in hand, he returned to Maine, only to discover that she, believing herself deserted, had married another.

Upon learning that his father had intercepted their letters, a confrontation ensued. Greenleaf Davis broke all ties with his family, leaving Lincoln forever. He had only the knapsack on his back and a newly-acquired Winchester repeating rifle. He hiked fifty miles north to the small village of Patten, but even this seemed too crowded for him. He continued another ten miles, and across the border into Aroostook County, where he finally built his secluded log home on the distant shores of Shin Pond.

That had been over fifty years ago, and by Alice's reckoning the old man was now at least in his nineties. His eyesight was fading, although he still wrote beautiful poetry, lines of cantos on the splendors of nature. In the wintertime he snowshoed into the village now and again for supplies or to participate in a local function. In the summer he rarely ventured beyond the lakes and woodlands. So that Alice half expected on such a night, that he might make his presence known, amid the gentle symphony of God's creatures.

Would she have waited for a man for nine years, even if letters hadn't been intercepted? Alice thought not, but perhaps she had never known truly great love. She'd had suitors, of course, who had wanted to marry her, and yet she turned each of them down in turn. Now she was over twenty, and she had been apprised by many a well-meaning friend or relative that if she remained so particular she might well spend her life as a school-teaching spinster.

For some reason, she found the notion that she should be branded a spinster altogether amusing. She brushed a mosquito away from her ear. She loved the simple life offered by the remote woods, the solitude to read, the opportunity to ignite young creative minds available through her position at The Academy. And yet, she could not imagine that she should never know any other life but this, her small pocket of the world. Would she never see Byron's Greece? The Assyrian Hills? The English Lake District which had so inspired Wordsworth?

There was only one road to those dreams, and that she knew. She would have to marry a man of means, and that probably meant Mr. George Callendar Reed of Boston, who although refined and somewhat interesting was not young. He was marginally attractive. Perhaps more intimate amorous activity deepened love in a way that she did not yet understand. This was an interesting, but wicked thought; however, if marrying Mr. Reed would offer her choices in this life, then she might do well to consider it. She would simply die if she had to wither away never knowing what was beyond the range of Patten, Maine.

George was inside the camp at this very moment drinking tea or spirits with Mr. Moody and her father. It had grown dark. She silently prayed that no one would come looking for her, as she was beginning to hear stirring within the walls. The camp seemed to be in another golden world, remote and somehow not quite real.

She remembered how Mr. Davis had come to their home in Patten a week or so ago, when the fiddleheads were still fresh. She had been mesmerized as the old man quoted his verse. He had been on his way to a debating society meeting in town, and when it was discovered that he was going to speak on the rights and socially equality of women, Alice sat straight up and in a voice that was louder than usual blurted out, "Good for you, Mr. Davis! Good for you, indeed!"

A shocked silence followed from the others, but Davis, encouraged, was oblivious to the reaction of the others. His cantankerous voice addressed Alice.

"Don't be a slave! Fight it, dear child! The Negroes have been emancipated; now it is the time of women. Don't let your strong mind be destroyed!"

She thought deeply of those words as George Reed clumsily walked down the banks towards the water. Bother, she thought. As he made her way towards her she smiled a polite greeting.

"What are you doing out here alone...Dear?" he queried with an awkward tenderness.

Don't be contrary, she coached herself. The world, the world, the world...

Aloud she said, "I'm listening for Hunter Davis's violin."

"Well, you shan't hear it anymore, Alice. Yesterday they took the old hermit to the alms house in town. He wasn't in his rightful mind." He caught the horror in her expression. "Well, it was for his own good."

In that moment she hated Mr. George Reed, but with force that cut the wilderness in her like a rope upon her neck, she squeezed that yoke with steady, invisible control.

"Mr. Reed," she began, "I think that you have come to ask something of, have you not?"

Davyne Verstandig

The Japanese Gentleman

Millay took a sip of water as a lemon slice drifted to the bottom of the glass. Once, many years ago, a Japanese gentleman stayed for a winter at the Paradise Inn. He was handsome, hair inkblack, old eyes, cheekbones of high certainty. He was quiet and would sit facing the sun, moving his chair at intervals, east to south to west. At times he would pick up a black pen and write a few minutes in a red leather journal. He drank his water with lemon and ate a daily round of bread. Millay watched him from the bar and from time to time glanced up to see how far the gentleman had moved his chair. Occasionally, he would smoke a cigarette that he took from a silver case. His lighter was inlaid with lapis lazuli.

He never brought a book to read. Journal, pen, cigarette case, and lighter lay on the table. Sometimes he would take deep breaths, inhaling the fragrance of lavender from the fields outside the village. He seemed patient. He wasn't waiting. He was sitting. He was established there in the sun on the patio moving slowly and deliberately through each day. Certainty and grace emanated from him. He would smile shyly at Millay, his eyes lowered.

One day, the morning he left on the ferry, he said to Millay, "The Taoists say that once you have told someone your feelings there is no more need of those words to be spoken again. I love you. I have been loving you everyday. I will love you forever. Arigato," and bowing slightly he crossed the street and boarded the ferry bound for the mainland. Sometimes someone showers you with love without touching you — covering you with the full gracious armor of love.

Millay refilled her glass with water from the carafe beside her bed. She removed the slice of lemon and bit into it, refreshed by its tartness. She replaced it with one from a white plate. Three slices of lemon left. Somewhere the Japanese gentleman was still loving her.

A monk is knocking at a door by moonlight (Jia Dao)

I go to answer
stumbling over cat
turning a cup of tea
into my ink pot
my brush tumbles
I open the door
only the moon

Lonesome Man

I had a friend once named Lonesome Man who lived on the edge of things. It was where he was comfortable. From the edge he could see into the middle of things, the life of things, and, at the same time, have emptiness at his back. He sat at the end of the table, never in the middle, the aisle seat at the movies or the theatre, the seat nearest to the door of the subway, bus, train, or plane. It gave him pleasure to walk with enough space behind him — to be at a distance from nearly everything. He could see better there he told me; things were clearer at the edge and quieter. As much as he needed space, he needed quiet, too. He lived on the edge of love, happiness, safety, and the edge of sadness.

One day I opened the door and Lonesome Man was slouching against the doorframe. He was back again, back in my doorway and perhaps my life. He was a drifter, a man who filtered through life, who smudged some days with his quiet; other days he carved each hour separate from the next. He was still handsome. I've always been a sucker for his driftwood grey eyes, his high cheekbones and that cleft in his chin. His hair was wild. He'd taken to letting it grow, then chopped it off in places. It was white, not salt and pepper. A two-day growth of stubble nearly hid the cleft. He wore a brown corduroy jacket, a blue denim work shirt, brown corduroy pants and hiking boots. I saw the snow falling just behind him. In his gloved hand, with the fingertips cut off, he held out a bottle of wine. "I remembered," he said, with a smile full of good memories. I must have had a quizzical look on my face as he continued, "I remembered today is your birthday."

I shook myself as though I'd been dreaming or lost in thought. I'd forgotten it was my birthday. How is that possible? Well, I live alone and stay somewhat isolated from others who might remind me. Some days I move through more slowly than others. Some days I mark hours, some days I mark them by dawn and noon and twilight and deeper evening but not the names of the days or the months. The look in Lonesome's eyes made me surrender to this gift, this gesture of remembrance.

"May I come in?" he asked in a tone of voice almost too polite for old lovers. He was still standing; bottle in hand, snow falling on his shoulders, waiting for some kind of response from me.

"Oh, of course. Come on in. You caught me by surprise "I said as I took the wine from him. "Thank you." I looked at the label. It was a Pommard, one of my favorites. Lonesome smiled. I reached over and brushed the snow from his shoulders and motioned for him to sit by the fire. He hung his jacket over the back of my desk chair, leaving his red scarf on. His eyes, the color of driftwood, were piercing and more like a wolf or a Malamute with the fire reflecting in them. I had two wing chairs, one on either side of the fireplace, and he chose one and I sat in the companion chair across from him. I picked up a corkscrew on the table and extended the bottle for him to open. He still hadn't said anything since "May I come in."

"How are you? It's good to see you," I said as he filled our glasses and we raised them, clicked gently, and made a wordless toast. "Were you just passing by?" I asked with a smile. It was unlikely since I lived on a dirt road off of a dirt road.

He responded with a silent laugh I could see in his eyes and spread across his face.

Years ago he had taken a vow of silence. He did this, he said, because he wanted to listen better to what the world was saying. I remember him telling me about the black Beat Poet Bob Kaufman, who took a vow of silence for seven years during the Viet Nam War.

Lonesome was here, drinking wine, smiling, listening, and waiting for something that I didn't think I could or would give him again. Tears fell from my eyes. I had chosen to live alone as he had chosen to keep silence. We would finish our wine and he would leave and I would remember. Then I'd continue to watch the snowfall and the fire blaze.

echoes and fragments

In silence I write words I cannot speak
I can't find the name for what I long for
I wonder if being too careful is harmful
In the lines of my face I see the edge of sorrow
  and the memory of laughter
Breathing ice slivers I watch silence falling in flakes
The stones I placed on the woodstove warm my bed
How complex simplicity can seem
What is that fragile fragrance of memory
I can't find the name for what I long for
I strain to hear silence
Can I make a poem of something that tastes like ashes
A deafening beauty beneath drag of wave —
  a rattle rumble of stones
Betrayal is a stone too hard to swallow

*

I'd like to write a poem but I don't know what it would say
I carry lovers and husbands inside me to places
  we were never together —
Is there anything left to be said I haven't said about jealousy and
  regret
Desire diminishes — I hardly remember its fire
What would happen if I were forced to listen
  to the sounds of torture
Is there any space at the edge of safety

A bowl of pink and orange peaches blushes in the light
of the full moon
Desire sleeps beneath forgetfulness
At the corner of regret and desire a wind withholds
the delivery of spring
I read your letter — rain streams from my eyes
Do the deaf recognize silence
Thoughts stream and bump into each other —
Your words try crossing my road
This is not the right time
This is the only time
The bruises of morning
I long for this something I cannot name

*

In a space of silence I learn what is
There are those I love who are shaking on an edge
Sleep pushed me out of her lap, walked away, left me stranded
in dusky morning hours and unfinished dreams
I make space for the emptiness filling me
I thought ours was a steadfast love
Watching you watching her
It doesn't help to remember love
Some days everything is a prayer
Loneliness is hollow longing deep
How do I capture what is gone

*

I don't know how this story begins or how it ends
Before I knew what God was there was salt water
What would it be like if bombs and guns felt guilt
Grief is a pulse

If I ate your words, really digested them, could I write your poems
Is it the aroma of baking bread I remember —
    or is it the anticipation of the taste of bread
On the median of the Penn Turnpike my gravel bitten brown calf skin
    vol 3 (of 8) of Byron's *Childe Harold's Pilgrimage* lies
In my dreams I never arrive
I must find the island of lost words

*

Beneath flickering stars lightning daggers and frogs
    speak of fleeting things
8 swans stir the pond
Clothed in torn sweater and words I wake
A leaf clings to the window waiting for flight   like me
Where is the boat that carries sorrow away
In the snow I cried for the love that tasted like spring
Sometimes only pleasure fills the empty cup of longing
Butterfly on a window of memory and sadness
A woman trembles in a distant country
I drink red wine until the stars weep   then everything begins again
Night leaks away

*

I must find the island of lost words

There are many letters that never get written

There are many letters that never get written and letters that don't get sent. This morning in the four o'clock time, which is holy and expansive, I write to you.

When I read you are with me.

When I see bare branches, feed the birds, watch ripples on the lake, smell wood smoke, tilt my face towards the sun, watch light move through the woods empty of leaves, hear the pop of a fire, close my eyes, breathe — you are with me.

You are in the turn of the pages, you are in the ink, in the dream, the closed musings in silent morning darkness, you are in the unspoken words, you hear what I cannot say, you understand when there are no words, you are with me on the other side moving back and forth between one kind of time and another — as I move into quiet which is not silent, you are with me. As light beckons me into day and darkness into evening, you are with me.

I am blessed knowing you all these years, having you with me, alongside me, inside and above me — having you wherever I am across time and the boundaries of place — here with me.

31

Dimitri Rimsky

The Night Caller

If Prometheus were Unbound
Where would he go?
Would he return to the lover
to whose hearth he first brought the fire?

Would she be there waiting for him?
Not likely.

Oh, at first She stayed close to him,
till the screams drove her Mad with despair,
till the flapping wings haunted her sleep,
till she could not face another day
of tending an endless wound.

So she took the embers
and left him on his rock.
Left him chained in the shadow of the bird
left him to suffer alone.

He understood.
He forgave her.
What else could he do?

And she walked away
till she couldn't hear him screaming
till the sun cast no shadows over her
till she broke the chains of love
and found a home in a distant world
and after some years she learned to
sleep without dreaming

So she was completely unprepared
when the knocking in the night called her from the hearthside,
called her from her lover's bed

Imagine her horror opening the door
to find him, collapsed on the threshold
gaping wound in his side
the dust swirling up in the wind of the beating wings.
Imagine her horror standing there
when he looked up at her
imploring to be taken in.
Safe from the reach of the bloody beak.

What would you do?
Oh certainly your first instinct would be to drag him in
to place him by the fire he suffered for
to clean his wounds, to hold him, to cry over him
to rock him in your arms

But what of her life.... Now?

What of the man calling to her from a distant room?
What of the terror of the screaming, flapping shadows?
What of a future forever pursued by relentless talons?
What of that!

No you think. No one could be that cruel.
But isn't it crueler still to ask her,
to expect her
to suffer forever with him?

Is the cost of love that high?
Is that the price she must pay for caring,
must she go on paying forever?
Isn't it fair that she too be unbound?

After all wasn't it he who defied the law?
Wasn't this really his punishment and his alone?

She had only complained of being cold!
She would have been as warm if he had stayed and held her.

Wasn't it he who betrayed her!
Wasn't his grand defiance really only an act of vain glory?
Wasn't her heart broken? Wasn't once enough?
She'd done what she could
but the screaming
the black wings,
the blood and anguish were too much.

He called to her again from a distant room
and she closed the door.

She would tell him
"It was only the wind."

Broken things

It's broken
Can you fix it
Sort of
Why don't you
Haven't gotten around to it
Nice chair wasn't it
That's why I keep it

How about this one
It's broken
Looks ok
I fixed it
sort of
Can I sit in it
Sure use this pillow
Oh!
And so it goes
Things break
Some from use
Some from disuse
Others of course from abuse
Neglect plays a big part
So does indifference
Life is hard
on inanimate objects

The living fair better

I mean to a point
they regenerate

Broken bones mend
chair legs don't
its simple
Even a broken heart
will heal

Somewhat
on its own

Ever seen a porcelain
statue
pull its self
back together?

No it just lies around
woeful
and fragmented
indefinitely
By the time
the Duco cement
comes out
it's lost some pieces
and it ends up
in a drawer
somewhere
I've got boxes
full of stuff like that

Why?
The answer (could be) sentiment
at least you would think so
but it isn't
isn't it really something else

A child's toy
we might understand

It broke
you held it up
imploring
Broke
you said
Don't worry dear we'll get another one
No
not good enough
I want this one
But its broken now
I don't care
and off you go
with your broken toy
and now here it is
still (broken)

Ok fair enough
perhaps that's where it begins
And so do those little lectures about
"How we take care of our things"
But the plain truth is
that things don't last
and obsessing about it doesn't help
Just as the Pharaohs

My roof leaks
it's broke
sort of
If it were skin
it would heal
eventually
The leak only gets worse
I have to fix it
eventually

This takes time
and effort
Maintenance
they call it

Do you have any idea
how much of your life
is dedicated to maintaining
inanimate things?

Lots
more than you realize
I'd venture a guess
that 80% of life
goes to breathing life
into lifeless things

Cars, big item
houses bigger still
highways huge
VCRs, microwaves, TVs,
forget it
No one even bothers
anymore

Replacement
if you don't think replacement
is a form of maintenance
you're in denial
Scary isn't it
How many toys
did you break
that you didn't keep
How many bikes
radios, glasses
What if you kept every car

you ever owned
Christ what a mess.
Get the picture
Every life is really
a junk yard
in transition
I love junkyards
curio shops you can't
even walk around in
Heaven

Funny little couples in Santa Monica
who live in a house made of
bottle caps and lipstick tubes
Sure why not

Crazy old ladies
found dead in a house
filled with everything
Every Thing they ever owned
Not crazy,
not crazy at all

Sentimental?
Every Waterbury Republican since 1903
I don't think so
I think it's something else

Ever talk to a junk dealer
or a curio shop owner
I don't mean some smarmy
antique dealer
I'll get to them
No, I mean the person
rattling around behind all that stuff
Ever notice how unpleasant they are

as if the open sign on the door
was an oversight
and you had just barged in on them
in the middle of some bizarre
ritualized act
of auto eroticism
with a 1932 Hudson
hood ornament

Sell anything?
Nonsense
Nothing even has price tags
But spend a few hours in there
poking around
and then
ask them about the 52,000
different iron doorstops
or the strange shaped tool with two blades
and wooden handle
and funny curved thing
sticking out of it
and the next thing you know
they're blowing dust off an old chest
that doesn't look
like its been opened for 30 years
and showing you stuff you can't imagine
And you're on the floor
rooting around
both ignoring
the couple that just walked in
with matching sweaters
tied around their necks
growling when they ask about iron door stops
Don't have any
What about this one?
50 bucks

Isn't that a bit high?
Take it or leave it
We'll take it, its perfect isn't it honey
Leave the money on the table
Do you take Visa?
Nope
It's not about the money

It's about old broken stuff
it's about toys in the attic
tools in the cellar
hubcaps and license plates
on the walls of the garage
It's about boxes
of mis-matched pieces
It's not about collecting
Hummels
or dolls
or baseball cards

It isn't about collecting
It's about broken things
discarded things
forgotten things
things that outlived their usefulness
or purpose
or even the lives
of anyone who ever knew
what they were good for
It's not about sentiment
It's about cherishing
the broken thing
because it's broken
because once it wasn't
Because once it Was something
meant something

It's about tragedy
and longing
It's about hope
and fidelity
It's about holding on
and worse
it's about failure and despair
and as life goes on
it was what was discarded
that we long for
and it is about that part of us
that was alive when it was not
broken
and it is about the part of us
that saw it break
and that part of us
that broke with it

And we mended
but there were pieces missing
It is after all
the broken things
that are the most human
of the objects we cherish
and they are parts of us
And I am suspicious
of people
who keep no broken things

how easily they discard
the no longer useful
the worn out
the thread bare
and torn
seemingly without remorse?

Oh, but how they prize
their Chippendale
Yep paid $50 bucks
for that iron door stop
Yeah, it's not about the value
it's about the caring

It's broken alright
but I might get around to fixing it
And when all is said and done
I may not have
fixed it all
but it wasn't for lack
of caring

Emelie Samuelson

Thanks a Lot, Weird Genetics

I'm twenty-five, but if you were to just look at the state of my hips and back, you'd think I was decades older. I have a lot of strange issues with my skeleton, most of which are caused by the fact that I have a very acute form of spina bifida. Don't worry, it's so mild that it isn't life threatening or anything, but it does come with its own issues. Essentially, I have an extra vertebra in my spine, and my tailbone never really...happened. I guess when I was still in my mom's womb my tailbone was all "NO! I'M NOT READY! I WANT TO BE MORE LIKE THE REST OF THE SPINE!" and then the rest of my spine was like "Dude, if you don't do what you're supposed to do, this girl is going to be born with a tail. IS THAT WHAT WE WANT, REGGIE?"

The end result? A sort of half-formed tailbone...thing. It's not noticeable in any way, unless you're looking at my x-rays, but it's a thing that sometimes causes problems.

For example, I woke up the other day and my hip felt like someone just popped it out of the socket and now it's refusing to go back in. And, because I know that whole song about all the bones being connected, it shouldn't surprise me that there is shooting pain and discomfort running up and down the whole left side of my body...which results in people staring at me when I think I'm alone as I try and bend my body into all sorts of weird positions to hopefully put my hip back in its rightful place. And this is a small town. People talk. So now I'm *that* girl.

And my hip decided to do this at a really not awesome time.

I work in a bookshop, and yesterday was Independent Bookstore Day. Indie bookshops across the country, including this one, were celebrating with tons of festivities. I planned many of our festivities, and one of those festivities was a Rad American Women Dance Party, because one of the exclusive merchandise items was a 7-inch LP inspired by the book, Rad American Women A-Z, which is an awesome book, and I suggest you rush to your local indie bookshop and buy it right now.

Anyway, I was doing my best on this very busy shopping day to not show how much pain I was in, all the while knowing that the grand finale would be a dance party, and that I was to be pioneering this dance party, so I was really going to have to shake it.

Oh, and did I mention that I had no pain meds with me?

Let's just soak this all in:

Spina bifida.

Rebellious hip bone.

Terrible back pain.

No meds.

LET'S BOOGEY.

I was about to panic for a moment, so I went into the back room to take a deep breath and to try and stretch my back and then I took to twitter:

@AwkwardlyAlive: My back is in the worst pain ever and I have to host a dance party for #bookstoreday in 3 hours. I WILL POWER THROUGH. I MUST DANCE.

1:53 PM - 30 Apr 2016

And all I really got in response was some nonsense about wildebeests that I'm still trying to make sense of...so twitter kind of failed me on that one. I think. I'm still not sure.

And then the time came, and — I kid you not, folks — no one showed up for this dance party. There were a few stragglers in the store, yes, but they were all very disturbed when I told them what was about to happen, because apparently people don't typically put dance parties and bookshops together, a fact that still saddens me to this day.

But you know what? I blasted Cyndi Lauper's "Girls Just Wanna Have Fun" and danced anyway. Because life is short.

Plus I was also hoping that if I danced, maybe I would move a certain way to pop my hip back into place.

Thinking and Feeling and Thinking About the Feelings

I *love* being emotional.

I understand this might be a bizarre thing to say, but it's true. I love having feelings. I love thinking about what I'm feeling and trying to figure out why I'm feeling it. My fiancé knows this well about me. I'm always asking him, "What are you feeling? What are you thinking? What are you thinking about what you're feeling? TELL ME."

And his response? Usually a blank stare while he chews his first bite of cereal in the morning.

Yep: I wake up like this, people. I wake up ready to talk about my emotions and I'm willing to have that conversation *all day long*.

This even goes for sad feelings. My sister and I will intentionally watch movies that make us cry. We call it "emotional yoga." Both her husband and my fiancé are baffled by this voluntary self-destruction, but we will defend it until the day we die, because sometimes feeling sad and crying feels *just so good*.

This has its drawbacks, though. Especially when you fall in love with someone who thinks that having feelings is a weird thing and that talking about them openly is even weirder. Fiancé isn't exactly the most vulnerable or verbal person I've ever met. It's not like he's an emotionless robot or anything. He has feelings, but getting him to talk about them can be like trying to train my dog to puke in the toilet. He doesn't get angry or upset about this (or anything in general), but it's just simply not a thing he feels the need to do. He's all about the logic and practicality. I'm all about those feelings.

Maybe this all just means that I'm a little bit more broken than he is and therefore I require a lot of analysis.

Some people would argue that I think too much and that I have a tendency to spiral inward or something like that, but I think that my constant emotional analysis is helping me grow.

I just think that if we're ever going to grow as people, we must look inward, right? If I stop looking at myself and wondering why I am the way that I am, how am I ever going to be better? Just like most people, there are things about myself that I don't love. There are things about myself that I wish were different. If I don't stop and check in on those things, I worry that I'll wake up one day and realize that I'm just the same as I've always been and that I haven't done anything about it...and then I'll just be a basket-case.

I'm not saying that I strive to be perfect. I know that that is an impossible goal, but I can always be striving to be better, right? And I think that allowing myself to feel things to the fullest extent and then to figure out why I'm feeling that sensation of anger or sadness or unadulterated joy will only lead to me being able to catch myself when I feel negativity rising up and redirecting it towards feelings of positivity and love.

All of this self-analysis has helped me to come up with little systems. When I feel a panic attack rising up, I've started to learn what I need to do so that I don't start yelling at someone who doesn't deserve it. I know to excuse myself from the room and go be alone for a few minutes when it gets really bad. When I start getting frustrated with someone, I've learned to remember that the only behavior I can alter is my own, and that has helped me to react in a more productive way.

All of this said, I'm still really working on it and I always will be. I'll always be working on myself. I'll probably always have panic attacks and I'll probably still get annoyed with other people and wish they would be different. But I'm working on it. I'm working on learning that Fiancé's way of expressing himself is different from mine and that both ways are okay. And I'm working on remembering that my dog is a not people, no matter how much we both think he is, and that he cannot be trained to run to the bathroom and puke in a toilet. It's simply not in his nature.

So what are you feeling? What are you thinking? What are you thinking about what you're feeling?

55

Fee de Merell

Delicious

A friend hugged me the other day, and said, "You smell delicious!" What was it that made me smell delicious? The faint, sweet scent of face cream and face paint, in medium beige, and soft rouge, and blue, and pink? My body lotion — some generic but possibly pleasing perfume? My hair products, mousse, and wax, and spray, or the gentle smell of hair lightly burnt from straightening irons? My deodorant? The one that is not supposed to smell or leave white streaks, but which does both? My actual perfume, that comes in a glass box and has a name so filled with hyperbole that it is meaningless, promising everything, but giving nothing, being, as it must, subsumed by all the other perfumes I'm realizing only now, probably cancel it out or turn it into something it was not when it was sitting in the bottle?

Or did she smell my indefinable and unique scent? Me. Am I delicious? Perhaps what she smelled was a combination of all of the above, and therefore still unique, because although I accept that I can't be the only person out of seven billion who wears this combination of lotions, creams, and sprays, I'm the only one who adds my indefinable me-ness to it.

And what does it all say about me? I'd like to think that I choose my scents to express who I am, who I'd like to be, who I want you to think I am. I'd like to think that if you happened to smell me, your subconscious would say, "Oh yeah, that is one edgy and confident woman who doesn't take any shit and radiates an inner strength and vitality that I for one, admire!" But to be honest, I get a lot of my products at the supermarket, on clearance, so the chances are, my scents do not give that sense.

My sense is that my scent is a confusingly pleasing mess of me, and based on this analysis, I've decided to invent a new fragrance. I'll call it, "Identity Crisis", and I'll market it in a multi-faceted, multi-colored bottle to women over forty who are just figuring out exactly who they are and what they want. Women who are done with taking any more shit in their lives. Women who are coming to accept that they have been, and will be, many things to many people, but to whom it no longer matters. I invite you all to spray yourselves liberally with Identity Crisis, and when it mingles with our other scents, we'll change its name to "Freedom". And I can promise you this: it will make you smell delicious.

Jumping Off Point

A few months after my marriage ended, I got involved with someone.

A few months after *that* it was over and I was wondering what the hell had happened. I was knocked sideways by the being together and the breaking apart. A divorced woman I know, who'd been there, done that, said, "Oh sweetie, it was your transitional. We all have one. It's a rite of passage."

It occurred to me that every relationship I'd ever had was transitional. Like cross country trains, taking me from one stage of my life to another. I've endured the interminable waiting at stations, and the racing along the platform, so worried I'll be too late that I jump on the first one I see, thinking another might not come along, and not thinking about where they're going or if they'll run out of steam before we get wherever I think we're headed. When they're too slow, or I finally see they're hurtling towards the destination of Tedium, Shitsville, instead of Perfect, Nirvana, I usually jump, but not until we're nearly there, because I can't see it, I can't see where we're going, I can't see any of it because I don't know, I don't know where I want to go and so I'm doomed to get the wrong train because I don't know how to make the right connection.

***

There are trains, and then there's the London Underground. Very different experiences. When I was young, I'd buy a ticket on the Underground, then spend hours just riding around...underground. It was bliss: the feeling of freedom, of wandering, of impulse with no pressure. I loved everything about the Underground: the tiny cardboard tickets, the escalators, so long and slow that there was time and space for endless advertisements all the way down, and the map that was everywhere, showing all the stations, all the different lines that crisscrossed under the city. The names were familiar, regal, alluring: Victoria line, Piccadilly line, Northern line, District, Circle, Central. I loved the puzzle of figuring out the various ways of getting to a given destination, stopping at the tiled and eccentric stations, seeing Sherlock at

Baker Street, picturing the elegance of Covent Garden or Knightsbridge, or making up vague impressions of other places just from the names. I've never been to Golders Green or Chalk Farm or Maida Vale, but it was even better to imagine them than visit them. They were all right there, just above me, but to be underneath was enough. When I dragged myself up those long escalators, surrendered my ticket, and trudged up the dirty steps towards the light, I always knew I'd left something beautiful behind. Down there, I was just me, and no one knew where I was. Only the stations knew. It was impossible for me to be going to the wrong destination, because I wasn't going anywhere. Up above, I had things to do, and people to be.

***

Because I used relationships to spur me from one place to the next, because I couldn't stay in my underground playground and I didn't know how else to navigate reality, and because I had no sense of how I really should be travelling, I had a lot of relationships. With unsuitable men. Unstable modes of transport. Years ago, the most intense, the most romantic, the most wildly dramatic of them all, involved London Underground stations, and it was (to torture the metaphor) a trainwreck. I knew where it was going, but I refused to jump. The last time I saw him, when we'd crashed and burned and exhausted ourselves in an orgy of guilt, regret, and bullshit, was when we said goodbye at Oxford Circus station. We said we loved each other, he went through the barrier, headed down the escalator, and I, anguished then, but reminded of Dustin Hoffman in "The Graduate" now, screamed his name because my heart was breaking, and he, romantic sucker, ran back up the escalator, and we clung to each other across the barricade, and some people laughed, and I didn't care and I sobbed against his chest. Now I laugh too, but at the time, it shattered my world and I always hated Oxford Circus after that.

This dangerous and dramatic man got in touch again, right after my transitional break-up, exquisitely on time, pulling into the station as I was sitting there on the platform, thinking maybe I was done with trains and it was time to drive myself around for a while. He said he still loved me, he thought about me all the time, that I was his fantasy, that we were soulmates. He invited me aboard, stretching out his hands and waving away the images of his wife and child like smoke.

I was tempted for a while. Then I thought about how I used to love to travel in my own aimless style, just me, underground, and I said no, that if I were going to be with anyone, I'd rather be their reality, not their fantasy, and anyway he'd already ruined one Underground station for me. So, I walked.

Yvonne

ome time ago, I had coffee with a woman I knew slightly and wanted to know better. We were talking about divorce when she asked how old I was.

"I'm forty-five," I said.

"Oh," she said, "I thought you were older."

I think I said, "Thank you," because I didn't know what else to say. Then I said, "I've had a rough life," which is sort of true, but I don't know if I said it to defend my old-looking face or to make her feel better about having no filter.

Later, after we'd said how nice it was to spend time together, and that we must do it again (even though I was beginning to have my doubts) I wondered whether her assumption had really bothered me. My ego was bruised, but not stung. Most of the rough life I mentioned was dominated by the quantities of booze and drugs I'd drunk, smoked, and snorted between the ages of thirteen and thirty-six, and I'd never consistently removed my make-up before going bed until I was at least thirty-five, so really, I did it to myself. The miracle is that I made it this far, more or less intact.

I've always looked older than I am, which came in very handy for pursuing my hobbies of smoking and drinking when I was younger (and in case you're wondering, it was irrelevant for the drugs: dealers don't usually ask for proof of age). Looking older was an aspiration until I hit thirty, then it became a more ambiguous asset. Until I hit forty, at which point I realized I'd entered that strange and untalked-about realm in which people (and by "people" I mean women) become invisible to a significant percentage of the population. I do not like being invisible. But this unwished for change can be its own reward. For example, I haven't had to endure a cat-call or a wolf-whistle for years. And if it did happen now, I wouldn't put my head down and wish for the ground to swallow me up (hell no!), because what I paid for with the currency of lost youth, perkiness, and smooth skin, was a sense of self, a sense of worth, and a sense of humor.

When I got to the "incredible invisible woman" phase of life, also known as "middle age", I started to really identify with women who'd stopped worrying and started kicking ass. Not just the likes of Gloria Steinem and Maya Angelou – phenomenal though they are – but other inspiring females who refused to settle for anyone else's expectations. One of my role models is Yvonne, a brown-and-white dairy cow from Germany who, in 2011, made a break for freedom after she was sold for slaughter. She became a fugitive, hiding in the Black Forest for weeks, cunningly evading all attempts to capture her, including the temptation offered by Ernest, a prize-winning bull who was, in the words of a German official, "the George Clooney of bovines". But Yvonne knew that freedom was more important than pheromones, and she kept her distance, seemingly contemptuous of such a pathetic ruse to imprison her again. When the allure of Ernest failed, her would-be captors also set out her sister and her son as bait, but she remained elusive.

2011 was a slow summer for the European media, and there was a lot of coverage of this story. My favorite photo of Yvonne is one taken from a distance (obviously). She's in a clearing, looking uncompromising and unafraid, or so I like to think. Making a stand for herself, and the hell with what the rest of the world wants.

One of the many joys of the whole Yvonne saga is that in the end she wasn't captured, but chose to leave the forest in her own time, for her own reasons. A farmer discovered her on the edge of his fields, gazing wistfully at a herd of his cows. She was saved from slaughter by an animal rights group (but perhaps she really saved herself) and now lives peacefully with some of her relatives on a farm in Bavaria.

Yvonne's "I don't give a fuck what you think I should do" attitude is something I'm embracing. It still seems that we're supposed to diminish as we get older, especially older than forty, but I'm getting in touch with my inner Yvonne. Finally, I don't care what anyone else thinks of me, because I'm a lot more interested in what I think of myself. Jim Morrison said not to take life too seriously, because no one makes it out alive, so like Yvonne, I'm just trying to stay in one piece while I'm here. Getting older is okay. *Looking* older is okay, and if I look older than I really am, wearing clothes with a little attitude, and hair that my sister calls, “courageous”, so much the better. You’ll just see me as a few years more fabulous. Or you won’t see me at all. And I’m okay with that.

65

Jane Darby

The Look-Back

The Look-Back is kind of a thing with you. You'll be standing on the corner of 79th and Broadway, nuzzling your boyfriend's ear with your nose, sharing some private joke, kissing him one last time. Finally, you stand back and say good-bye. You turn, the both of you, and walk your separate ways. But you always look back. Looking to see if he looks back. He never does, so you continue on your way, disappointed.

It probably comes from the movies: one of those tropes that embedded itself into your ideas about love and romance. But the Look-Back is a very real thing, a way of saying, "Even though we're parting, we are still connected."

To date, none of your boyfriends have been practitioners of the Look-Back. It never occurred to one, and the others hadn't even heard of it. But you are not looking for a practitioner; you are looking for an *artisan* who speaks the language you speak: a wordless yearning for experience, a curiosity about a certain kind of fluency in love.

"There are some things in life that you will yearn for, but you will never, ever get," an older woman tells you. "That yearning, that longing laced with despair, is the important part. Life is lived in the yearning, not in the having."

You worry this might be true, but you are a creature of hope. And while the having may last no longer than a heartbeat, you swear that on the day your Look-Back is met with his own lingering gaze, you will change your plans, cancel all appointments, and run at the speed of light back into the arms of love.

Ugly

It happened in the late eighties, at a time when a certain news story broke, a horrific case of child abuse that was splashed across the front pages of all the tabloids.

Lucy, who usually stuck to *The New York Times*, was suddenly knee-deep in three-inch banner headlines and lurid photographs. She knew, given her current state of mind, that she would be better off avoiding the story, but something compelled her to seek it out.

At first, Jim responded with a mixture of bewilderment and patience. When he came home to the apartment a fourth night in a row, however, to find her on the sofa, clutching their five-month-old daughter, newspapers strewn on the floor and Lucy's face puffy and awash with tears, he snapped.

"For Christ's sake, Lucy. Give it a rest."

"It's just..."

"You haven't even changed out of your pajamas today."

"Now they're saying that she wasn't legally adopted. He was supposed to place her, but he just kept her for himself."

"You haven't showered in days. The place is a mess..."

"So he could use her as his personal punching bag."

"What's that smell?"

Lucy held up the front page of *The Post*.

"Look at this. Look at his wife. Look at her face. How many times do you think her nose has been broken?"

Jim dropped his briefcase into the armchair and reached for the baby. As soon as he pulled her close, he held her out again at arms' length.

"Jeez, Luce. She's carrying a huge load. When was the last time you changed her?"

The baby caught the sharp edge of his tone, turned her mouth down, and released a high-pitched moan that threatened to escalate into a full-blown wail. Jim shushed her, kissed her forehead, and carried her down the hall to her room.

"Did you know he was a lawyer?" Lucy called after him. When he didn't answer, she turned her attention to the photograph on the front page.

The woman's face looked like a lump of clay that had been squeezed hard and thrown against a concrete wall. There might have been a time when her features were fine and sharp; she might have been pretty once, but now she looked grotesque, like one of those shrunken heads that children carve out of apples at Halloween and leave on windowsills to dry.

"Did you know we're down to two diapers?" Jim hollered from the baby's room.

Lucy sighed and shuffled the newspapers into a pile.

The next morning Lucy and Jim saw each other for only a moment. They were passing in the hall, she on her way to the bathroom, he to work. With his hands full, he leaned in to give her a good-bye peck.

"Katy still asleep?" he whispered.

"Wouldn't you be asleep if you'd woken up screaming every two hours?"

"Well. Try to get out today. Maybe take a walk in the park."

"What's that?" Lucy nodded at a white plastic bag Jim was holding.

"The trash. What did you think it was?"

"They're in there, aren't they?"

"I just think it would be better if you read something else for a change. Maybe a book. "

"I'm not a child, you know." Lucy reached for the bag, but Jim dodged her hand and headed for the door.

"Enough with this junk. You want more, go out and buy it."

While the baby slept, Lucy sipped from a cup of decaf and stared out the window at the street below. The mimosa and ginkgo trees next to the curb had lost their leaves. They stood bare, almost shivering, locked in their square pits of hardened earth and tied down with wire, as if they were in danger of pulling up their roots and hightailing it upstate to the country. Rain from the night before had left rivulets of iridescent water running in the gutters. She wished she could dissolve and slip down the storm drain along with the rest of the runoff. Soon it would be Thanksgiving. Jim's parents would fly in from Ohio. The thought of them, the shopping, the cleaning, the cooking, the holiday hubbub, the forced cheer and endless advice exhausted Lucy.

Jim's mother, who attended a mega-church that preached the gospel of prosperity, would ask Lucy about her plans. Maureen's devotion to goal setting manifested itself in ways large and small, from daily to-do lists to five- and ten-year "stated objectives". Once, during a visit to their house in a suburb outside Cincinnati, she had shanghaied Lucy into watching a motivational video on the subject, as if the hand of her efficient god could reach out to Lucy through the TV screen.

"Doesn't that just make you want to get up and get going?" Maureen chirped. "Boy, I tell you, after I watched that thing the first time, I sat myself down right here at this table and mapped out my whole business plan for my greeting card company. I'll tell you this much: it sure was a lifesaver. Kept me from going crazy after the kids moved out. Kept me from going off the deep end."

Jim's father, who rarely talked, released a low rumbling sound from his throat. Lucy turned to him and asked, "What was that, Bill?" But he just shifted his weight in his recliner and continued to stare at the blank TV screen. A piercing cry from down the hall roused Lucy to her feet. Even at the door of the bedroom, she could tell the baby needed changing. After that, she'd need to nurse, then another change, then sleep, then up with a cry, then nurse, then change and again and again as it had been all night, as it would be all day, as it had been for five months, as it would be for as long as Lucy could imagine. She picked up the baby and carried her to the changing table.

When she untaped the diaper, Lucy saw the reason for Katy's rage. A fiery rash spread from her crotch down her thighs. It reminded Lucy of a sunburn she'd gotten when she and Jim had spent a day at Jones Beach back when they were dating. The next day, Lucy had lain in bed with the chills, her skin tight and sticking to the sheets. Jim had stayed with her, arranging cold, damp washcloths over the worst spots and telling weak jokes as she slipped in and out of sleep. Would he do that for her now, she wondered? With all her loose baby fat, oozing breasts, and stretch marks? She couldn't remember the last time she and Jim had touched.

Ignoring the baby's ongoing wails, Lucy wiped her clean and spread ointment on the rash. It wasn't until she reached into the drawer for a fresh diaper, that she remembered she'd used the last one sometime around five o'clock in the morning.

"I wonder if I could ask you a huge favor." A sliver of her neighbor's face peered at Lucy over the door chain. She glanced at the name under the peephole.

"¿Por favor, Senora Morales?" The door closed and after a brief jangle of metal, reopened to reveal a middle-aged woman in a pink uniform, unsmiling. Waiting.

Lucy was suddenly aware of how she must look, barefoot, hair uncombed, still in her pajamas, or what passed for pajamas these days: a pair of boxers and an oversized tee-shirt, holding a whining baby. Katy's rump was bare, and the grease from the ointment had left a dark smear on Lucy's shirt.

"Hola. I was hoping ... yo quiero ... necessito..."

"English."

"What? ¿Que?"

"Speak. English."

Lucy released a small laugh. "Oh, thank God. I've run out of diapers. I was hoping I could ask you to watch my daughter for a few minutes while I run out to the store."

The woman's eyes shifted from Lucy to the baby. "Come in."

Lucy followed the woman down the long hallway that ran the length of the apartment. The layout was a mirror image of Lucy's flat with tiny bedrooms sprouting off the hall until it opened out to the front rooms. In Jim and Lucy's apartment this was a single, large, loft-like space with an open kitchen and high ceilings. It was the relative expanse of the room, in fact, that had been the selling point for them. That and the price. They were pioneers, their broker had told them, adventuring into the wilderness of the inner city with its bodegas, salsa music, and sidewalk games of dominoes that stretched long into the night.

"With more young couples like you moving in, this will all be different in no time," the broker had said. "Already there's a D'Agostino opening up on Broadway. It's the sponsor's goal to sell off all the rental units within five years." She nudged Jim. "You could run for the co-op board."

In the neighbor's apartment, however, there was no such opening up of space. The hallway ended in a warren of three small rooms: kitchen, dining room, and living room. The woman gestured for Lucy to sit on the sofa, which was upholstered in a dull print and covered in sturdy, clear plastic. She opened the lid of a wicker chest that doubled as a coffee table and pulled out a towel, which she held out to Lucy.

"For the baby. For her bottom." When Lucy hesitated, she added, "Don't worry. It's clean."

"No. I just..."

The woman shook her head. "Like this." She folded the towel in half lengthwise and placed it between Katy's legs. "Excuse me now, please. I am cooking. I will be back in a minute."

Lucy jiggled Katy on her lap and looked around the room. She supposed it would be safe enough for her to leave the baby here. Mrs. Morales — she assumed she was a Mrs., though she'd never seen any sign of a Mr. Morales —had always seemed pleasant. They had never exchanged words, just imperceptible nods and fleeting smiles in the elevator before they lapsed into watching the numbers light up over the door. Even here in the woman's living room, Lucy could find little evidence of her private life. There were no books or magazines, no reading material at all, for that matter, not even a Bible. No rumpled blankets or half-consumed cups of coffee, no wadded-up tissues. The room was like a museum. The linoleum floor was clean and covered with a rug that Lucy had seen at one of the sidewalk sales on Amsterdam Avenue. The only indication of the woman's life beyond this room sat on a sideboard across from the sofa, a collection of framed photographs of a dark-haired girl at various stages of life. In one, she was an infant in her christening gown, lying on her back in a sea of frothy lace, arms thrown back in surrender. In the next, she wore a frilly white dress, clutching a prayer book and rosary beads in her gloved hands, her hair pulled back in a tight bun, her mouth frozen in her first communion smile. In another, she had become a young woman, standing erect in a cap and gown, this time holding a diploma. There were no other subjects in these pictures. No photos of a mother or father, no family at all. It was as if this girl had grown up under the stewardship of an invisible hand.

Lucy looked at Katy, who stared beyond her to the overhead light, her gurgling lips shiny with drool. It seemed impossible that she would ever make it to any of her own milestones. Lucy considered it a triumph when she managed to get through the day without killing her. There were so many disasters lurking just around the corner. If she didn't drop Katy on her head or accidentally poke something through her fontanel, she might pass some environmental toxin to her through her breast milk or come in one morning to find she had been taken by crib death. Yet, right here in front of her was photographic proof that it could be done. That somehow, by hook or by crook, the young inherited the world.

The woman appeared in the doorway carrying a thermos.

"Your daughter is beautiful." Lucy nodded toward the pictures.

A curious expression flickered across the woman's face, but she said nothing as she set the thermos on a side table next to her purse.

"Is she in college now?"

The woman turned slowly to face Lucy. "She is with God. In heaven."

Lucy's heart froze. "I'm so sorry. I didn't know."

The woman shook her head as if to ward off any gestures of pity. "Twenty minutes."

"I beg your pardon?"

"Please be back in twenty minutes. I cannot be late for work."

"Yes, of course. Thank you so much." Lucy stood and handed Katy to the woman, who took her and for the first time, softened her expression.

"Miss."

"Yes?"

The woman looked her up and down. "Maybe you should change your clothes before you go to the store."

On the street the city thrummed, punctuated by sirens, car alarms, and horns. People walked at a steady clip without bothering to look at her. Just as well. Lucy ran her fingers through her hair, unable to remember if she'd combed before she left. She had taken the woman's advice and returned home to squeeze into the one pair of non-maternity jeans that fit. She couldn't locate a clean shirt, so she threw on an old down jacket that was too small. Unable to zip it up, Lucy held it closed at the throat as she quickened her pace.

The line in the grocery store was long and slow moving. The only clerk on duty was an unsmiling girl with heavy make-up that accentuated the corrugation of acne scars on her cheeks. Lucy had been waiting for at least ten minutes, and there were still two people in front of her. She didn't look, but she could feel the impatient heat of those behind her. Once she'd gotten inside the store, she had managed to calm herself with assurances that Katy was safe, that all was well. But now in line with nothing to do but wait, she realized that she was going to make Mrs. Morales late for work.

She wondered how the girl had died. Had it been a long illness or sudden death by accident? Had a jealous boyfriend done her in, or a stranger, one of those awful predators you read about in the news? Lucy shook her head. It was too much, too horrible.

The line to the cashier inched forward. Lucy would be next. She began to put the diapers on the belt, but something stopped her. A strong, sour odor — the smell of decay — coming from the woman ahead of her.

Lucy had noticed she was old, but hadn't realized until now that she was a bag lady, hunched under many layers of grimy clothes, her gray matted hair sticking out from under a knit cap. She had placed a head of celery on the belt and was now digging through her change purse as she hummed tunelessly and occasionally spoke in the direction of her left breast.

"Now, where did that other dime go? Hmm? You saw me put it in here. Did you eat it? Couldn't you wait? Huh?"

She was ancient and wholly unkempt, with skin like weathered canvas that fell in folds over her jowls. A profusion of white whiskers bristled from her chin and upper lip. *Hag.* In an earlier century, Lucy thought, this woman would have been hanged as a witch. Today, she was merely forgotten, invisible until you got close enough to pick up her scent.

Lucy turned her gaze away and caught sight of the tabloids stacked in the racks above the gum. There he was, the child killer. The wife beater. The headline beneath his chin read, *He Snorted Cocaine While They Bled.* He seemed to be staring right at Lucy, his expression scornful under his smear of a mustache: *What are you looking at?* The gall of his self-righteous indignation.

The old woman had finished her business. She tucked the celery under her arm, collected her bags and bundles from the shopping cart, and turned her back on it in a gesture of abandonment. Lucy tossed a quick apology over her shoulder to whoever was behind her, backed up with the cart, and left the line for a few steps to push it out of the way. When she returned to her place, she found it had been taken.

For a moment, she lost her bearings.

"Excuse me. I think I was ahead of you."

A tall man in a Brooks Brothers suit wouldn't even look at her. "Well, you aren't anymore." He continued to place his items on the belt.

"But I was right behind that woman."

He turned slowly to articulate his contempt. "You left the line and gave up your spot."

Lucy looked at the column of blank faces behind him. She could go to the end of the line and make Mrs. Morales really late for work, but she felt an urgency to get back. Besides, there was something about this man, his natty dress and salt and pepper hair neatly coiffed in a white man's Afro, his manicured nails and Italian shoes, his arrogance that compelled her to press the matter.

"No. I was just moving the cart out of the way."

"And by doing so, you left the line, and I rightfully stepped in to keep things moving." His eyes traveled down to her feet. "Some of us have places to be, you know."

Heat crept into Lucy's face. "I have places to be."

"There's no point in arguing with me." He leaned in close enough for her to smell his cologne. "I have a very legal sort of mind."

"That's hardly any recommendation." Lucy's eyes flicked to the tabloid.

The man faced her completely now, squaring off for a fight. "Well, like it or not, I'm here. Deal with it."

Secretly, Lucy had already accepted defeat, but she was unwilling to go down silently. "You're very mature."

"And you," he said, pulling a jar of tomato juice from his basket, "are very ugly."

"What?"

"Look at you." He raised his voice and addressed the entire store. "I didn't know there was a trailer park in Manhattan."

The other customers in line maintained their indifference, but Lucy thought she could hear stifled laughter. A roaring grew in her head, and she couldn't be sure she was hearing him correctly. "All I'm trying to tell you is that I was in line ahead of you --"

"Uh, don't look now, but you're leaking." He nodded at her breasts. Lucy looked down and saw two damp circles the size of silver dollars, spreading around her nipples. She pulled at the jacket and covered herself with the package of diapers. Just as she was about to retreat to the back of the line, a flash of green smashed onto the man's head. Celery leaves rose, then fell onto his hair and the padded shoulders of his suit.

He turned around. "What the hell do you think --?"

"Manners!" The old woman thrust the truncated head of celery into his face. "Didn't nobody ever teach you no manners?" She stabbed the air with each word, the celery stopping millimeters from his nose.

"You crazy, old..."

The woman, unimpressed, calmly reached into the folds of her coat and drew out a rat. It sniffed the air and squirmed in her grasp. She thrust it into the man's face. "Now, shoo. Scat! Scram!"

With a cry, the man staggered back and did an odd, wobbly dance as he grabbed at the magazine rack for balance. His hand basket got in the way, and he fumbled the bottle of tomato juice. It smashed onto the floor, juice exploding in all directions.

"Goddammit!" His shoes and pants were splattered with the red mess. He stood there, cursing as he attempted to shake the worst of it off of his trousers.

Lucy stepped into his place in line.

"What do you think you're doing?"

"You left the line and gave up your spot."

"Wait a minute --"

"And I rightfully stepped in to keep things moving." She looked at the people behind her and nodded at them. "We have places to be, you know."

"There is no way..." He tried to shoulder his way in front on her, but Lucy stood her ground.

"There's no point in arguing with me," Lucy said, locking eyes with him and speaking slowly. "Like it or not, I'm here. Deal with it."

"C'mon, buddy, move it!" someone a few heads back yelled.

The man blushed, his skin reddening through the freckles on his forehead. His glare wavered, and then broke. "Oh, to hell with it," he muttered, kicking a shard of glass aside as he picked his way through the pool of juice and exited the store.

The bag lady offered some celery to her rat and restored him to his hideaway in her coat pocket. "See that? Mr. Big Shot's not so big now. Got to stand up in this life. Got to stand up to the fuckers of the world," she declared as she trundled out the door.

On the walk home, Lucy thought about the moment when she had stepped back into the line. It had happened like a series of clicks, as with a shifting of chambers, a change in the machinery. It had pared her down to her essentials, stripping her of gender, race, age, class. Everything around her dropped away, as well: the other people in line, the bag lady and her rat, the checkout girl; until all Lucy knew were the man's eyes, which flickered with startled recognition, as if he were suddenly seeing himself through a different lens. She wondered if he hadn't been on the verge of tears.

When Lucy found the door to Mrs. Morales's apartment ajar, her stomach lurched.

"Hello?" Her voice echoed off the walls of the long hallway.

"In here."

She found Mrs. Morales sitting on the sofa. She was neither angry nor impatient. Instead, she was holding Katy in her arms and humming a soft lullaby as she rocked gently back and forth. Slowly, she raised her head and smiled at Lucy.

"She is a good baby. So sweet."

Lucy eased herself onto the cushions next to Mrs. Morales and stroked the top of Katy's head. She was such a beautiful girl

"I brought you some money," she whispered. "So you can take a taxi to work."

"There is no need."

"No. I want to."

They sat quietly, mesmerized by Katy's sleeping warmth and trust.

Joe Connolly

After the Race

I was dejected and feeling sorry for myself after being dropped again. The van ride back to campus was long and boring; I kept my ear buds in and alternated between pretending to sleep and actually catching a few uncomfortable z's.

I was in no mood to go back to my room, and I certainly didn't want to contend with studying chemistry, so after we piled out of the van I pedaled down to the shop to see Jim. I got there a few minutes before he was going to close up. The radio was tuned to a classical station, the sound filling the otherwise empty and quiet shop. A half-eaten box of cold sesame noodles and an iced tea sat beside the cash register. Jim was working on an old commuter bike.

"How'd you do?" he asked as I walked back to the repair area.

"I got dropped. Again."

He didn't even look up and kept making dérailleur adjustments on the bike in front of him. I didn't bother to fill in the details. I was tired of making the same mistakes over and over again, tired of being dropped. There had to be some secret, something I was missing.

"I always feel like I'm either over-geared or under-geared," I said. "What gear am I supposed to use on a hill?"

"The right one," said Jim. He spun the pedals with his hands and clicked through the gears quickly.

If he was trying to be funny, I wasn't up for it. I could feel my self getting hot, so I unzipped my team jacket.

"What's the right one?" I asked, hoping for a simple, direct answer, preferably just a number.

"The one that goes fast," he said.

And just like that he broke my will and I gave up, just like I did when I stopped pedaling and sat up, watching the group ride away from me on the first hill of the morning's race. I had the same feeling: a helpless futility with a tinge of rage. I picked up a small piece of cable and started winding and unwinding it around my index finger.

Jim took the bike off the rack and wheeled it out towards the register. I stayed where I was, focused on the self-inflicted pain in my bright red finger tip. He locked the front door, flipping over the sign to "Sorry, we're closed" and turned off the radio. He straightened out a few tools on his bench, then grabbed a broom and started sweeping.

There was no sound except for the scraping of the broom on the wooden floor; he was making small piles of debris, with colorful bits of cable housing punctuating the dirt and dust like confetti. After a few minutes, I couldn't bear the silence.

"I'm serious," I said. "I really want to know. What's the right gear?"

"How am I supposed to answer that?" Jim replied. "You're the one riding the bike."

I wanted to curse, or hit him, or throw a bike off the wall, or maybe all three, but I managed to stay put. I grabbed a wrench and drummed it on the repair stand. I knew there had to be an answer, and I bet he had it. Week after week I was getting dropped, yet there were dozens of guys who made it up every hill in the pack. I tried big gears and it didn't work, I tried little gears and that didn't work either. If Jim would just tell me what to do, I'd do it.

After a few more minutes of sweeping and silence, Jim finally spoke up.

"Look, Alex," he said, "the only person who knows the right gear is you. Nobody else can decide that for you."

I didn't say anything but I was feeling frustrated and stupid, because even though I kept trying, I wasn't getting it right. I had plenty of crummy results and DNF's to prove it. He put away the broom and sat on a stool.

"There are infinite situations, and infinite circumstances. You asked about a hill. Is it a long hill or a short hill? A steep hill or a gradual hill? Are you feeling strong or feeling tired? There is no one right answer."

He stood up, and switched off the lights in the repair area.

"The main thing is, *you* need to decide. You're the one on the bike, so it's up to you to figure out what will work. You need to make up your mind. And then you need to stop worrying about it and commit. Whatever you pick, have confidence and just go for it. And if it doesn't work, make a change. It's really not that complicated."

He was walking towards the front of the shop, so I got up and followed him. Just before he unlocked the door to let me out he said "The worst thing you can do is second guess yourself. Make up your mind and then pedal your ass off."

He unlocked the door and opened it.

"Now get out of here. I'm closed."

Living with Phantoms

David got his toes cut off.

His father called me early one Sunday morning. I was driving north on Route 8, winding along the Naugatuck River, heading to the Berkshires to go skiing with my daughters. The girls were in the back seat, immersed in a movie. My cell phone rang from its perch on the empty passenger seat. I recognized the number but couldn't quite place it.

"Your friend is in a tough spot," a familiar voice murmured, "can you help us?"

Although I hadn't spoken to him in years, I recognized my friend David's father. He told me there had been an incident, and it looked like David was going to lose his toes. He was calling because they were concerned about his medical care. Should they fly him from Boulder to Boston? My mind raced, trying to imagine what calamity had befallen David. I was confused by his questions, trying to make sense of the story while struggling to hear the scant details over poor cell service and the sound of the video. I promised him I'd speak with a physician friend of mine to get an objective medical opinion, and that I would phone his son. Keeping one eye on the road, I groped around for a pen, and scrawled David's number on a scrap of paper before hanging up.

I calculated what time it was in Colorado; early but not too early to call. Finally, I dialed the number his father had relayed. David picked up on the first ring.

"I knew it would be you," he said in a barely audible whisper.

***

Ours was a two-wheeled relationship, delicately balanced and kept upright by movement and speed. Our mothers introduced us, but our friendship was forged on our bikes.

I was a student at Boston University when I began riding. I bought my first racing bike at Laughing Alley, a funky little bike shop on Harvard Avenue. It was a hand-made Italian frame, a metallic orange Viner. I used to go down to the shop late at night (when I should have been studying) and stare longingly at the frame through the metal security grates over the shop windows. The bike cost $800; when I finally purchased it I had $2 left to my name and zero regrets.

When I met David, he was taking electrical engineering classes at a local college. He was a begrudging student; I suspected he was getting his degree at his parents' behest. David made it clear that he would rather be outside — doing almost anything — than in a classroom. When it came to cycling, he had been riding and racing for years. Slightly awed by his self-proclaimed knowledge and experience, I became his willing acolyte.

David always pushed harder and went farther than me; farther from home, deeper in to the woods, closer to the edge. It seemed he was always returning from or heading off to go hiking or kayaking. He thought nothing of living in his car and would sleep anywhere he happened to pull over. He definitely had a bit of a wild streak, and was simultaneously meticulous and reckless.

We rode every night, as soon as we got out of our summer jobs. On one of our first rides together we were hammering down Charcoal Avenue towards Fenn's Pond. Inches from David's rear wheel, I struggled to stay in his slipstream. Suddenly the familiar sound and feel of pavement was replaced by the alarming flutter of dried leaves in my spokes and the ping of sand and pebbles against my rims. I was too tight, too focused on David's wheel, too new to the subtleties and finesse it took to handle a bike at high speed. For a moment the world seemed to move in slow motion, and in that instant my desire to stay on David's wheel conquered my fear of crashing, and I managed to stay upright. The rush of adrenaline was intoxicating.

During my senior year we went to Florida for spring break. While other kids were cruising the beaches and bars, we pedaled warm but boring miles at a preseason camp over the featureless roads of central Florida. The conditions were spartan: wooden cabins with bunk beds, crude showers, a small pool. None of it mattered; we were there to ride.

Our days were spent on the road, accumulating miles in our legs. We did skill sessions, learning to start quickly and accelerate powerfully, counterbalance while steering through a corner, to brake smoothly. We practiced the basics of riding in a pack. Keep your head up. Look around the rider in front of you. Keep your body and your grip loose.

When our training was done, David flirted with the one girl at the camp or worked on his bike. When it came to his equipment, he was fanatical. He worked in a bike shop and was a capable mechanic. He carried a toolbox with an entire collection of specialized bike tools in the back of the family station wagon. There were cone wrenches, spoke wrenches and a pedal wrench. He had a crank puller, a bottom bracket remover and freewheel removers. But what fascinated me most was something you wouldn't expect to find in a toolbox: an old toothbrush. David kept it — and used it regularly — to clean the hard to reach areas on his bike, which was always immaculate.

***

When I spoke with David about his incident he was uncharacteristically restrained. He relayed the story, unembellished. "I screwed up," he began. He had gone cross country skiing alone — his first mistake. He then got lost in the Colorado woods, moving in circles and unable to gain his bearings. Eventually, he came upon a familiar camping lodge. By then it was dark and everyone inside was asleep. "I didn't want to bother anyone," he said. "My feet were already frozen, and I knew I was screwed." So he made his way to his car and drove himself to the hospital. He talked about the pain, and then moving beyond pain, and then to somewhere beyond that. The whole ordeal lasted less than twelve hours.

"I should have known better," he said quietly, in disbelief.

I had experienced extreme weather with David before. We went skiing at Stratton with my younger brother. We parked at a remote lot and jumped on the back of a shuttle, an open wagon pulled by a pick-up truck. It was shockingly cold, piercing and intimidating. After a few frigid runs, we took a break at a mid-mountain lodge. Impervious to the conditions, David waited outside and unzipped his down parka, claiming he needed to vent. My brother and I retreated to the warmth of the lodge. Our goggles fogged up immediately and our boots clunked on the stairs on the way to the men's room. When he took his gloves off, my brother's fingers had swollen and looked like purple sausages. I was alarmed and concerned; when we made our way back outside and reported this to David he was nonchalant.

Driving home in his trusty station wagon, David refused to turn up the heater. I was as cold and miserable in the car as I had been on the slopes. I was exasperated when he stopped at a self-service car wash near home. As I sat shivering inside, he hosed off the salt and grime from his car, ice forming in seconds. When he got back inside he smiled. "Always take care of your gear," he said, "no matter what."

The next morning, when I got up to go to work, I shaved. As I looked in the mirror my cheeks were scabbed over from the cold and wind. The line between pleasure and pain was always blurred with David.

***

Though we haven't spoken in more than a year, I can't stop thinking about David's toes. I wonder what his feet look like, how he walks, if he can balance. I wonder if he needs special shoes. There's more to this than simple curiosity; somehow *his* loss feels like a loss to me. His mishap seems like the most unlikely of events, yet almost inevitable. It occurs to me he could have died alone in the woods on that cold December night. Given that, losing his toes doesn't seem so bad.

Physicians report that when amputees lose a body part more than 80% experience phantom pain, the sensation that the limb is still there. Sometimes it hurts, or itches, or burns. Sometimes it just feels like it is *there*, not gone. Evidence suggests this feeling can last for a lifetime.

Karen LaFleur

Stories "Ella-Jean", "Terry" and "Rebecca"
are from the artist's *Night Time* collection of women's voices
and originally exhibited as text/image artworks.

ELLA JEAN

"That kid ain't worth a half-spit in a can," my father said the night Nathan asked me to marry him.

I was eighteen, shiny and new, and Nathan drove a Detroit Special, a cream over red with tail-lights that cometed through the dark. Moving-always-moving that's how I remember Nathan and I longed to go with him to see what lay beyond the stop signs of Dylan County.

So we began...
behind a fence,
under a tree,
backlit by bedroom window light,
laughing on fender-top,
his hips against mine.

And for a moment my world stopped waiting for someone to care.

I asked my father's permission to marry out of respect for my mother. She wouldn't dare give her consent without his and I wasn't about to make her life any harder.

"No," was all my father replied.

Nathan stepped forward but I pulled him away. Instead I left home in a tire-spin that peeled a final goodbye in a hail of pebble and stone. That night Nathan and I drove through every stop sign that came our way, careening under a starlit sky, night-driving all the way to Coopersville by the drive-in theater on Route 93. We traveled fast on a beam of incandescent light, up over hill and into the soft of everywhere all at once. We were lovers chasing down journey's end, only to pull-up short on the backside of a waning moon.

Nathan loved to drive but he loved me more. So when our first child came he sold his car to a man over in Bakersfield. Then we settled down and held onto each other tight against the rotation of the world. That's something my father never understood.

That sometimes you've got to give up what seems important for that other part you know is right.

REBECCA

Outside,

snow whispers to the ground.
There's no fury left in the storm.
No gale to mark its passage.
No battering against these wooden walls to be let in.

It's over.

Only the tiniest of flakes drift in the night air
like after-dust floating back to earth and freezing to the landscape.

Inside,

there's a window at the top of the stairs.
I feel my way by moonlight until my hand touches the curve of trunk.

I open the lid.
My fingers lift a bundle onto my lap.
Fifty-three postcards tied with silk ribbon.
By moonlight I read each one.

"Meet me in Vegas," he wrote in '75.
Paris.
Milan,
Denver,
Cardiff by the Sea."

I take a postcard from my pocket dated 2004.
"Meet me in Tucson," he writes.
"Yes," I pen in the margin.

Then I place this postcard on top all the others,
retie the bow
and return the collection beneath the lid.

Outside,

a December moon disappears behind gossamer white.

TERRY

School bus yellow flickered across kitchen wallpaper.

Orange juice, a carton of milk and a cereal bowl with a super-hero tossed in upside-down his head twisted on backwards.

On the bottom of the hero's shoe read the words "not for young children" stamped in blue ink.

And I wondered, as the musical score to a 1930's film played from the TV screen in the living-room...

"It had to be you ..."

"It had to be you ..."

"Yes, it had to be youuu."

Peanut butter stains smeared the countertops and dishes waited in the sink to be cleaned. But I ignored them and instead walked my index and next finger in a sassy-sway dance in time to the music - "it had to be youuuu" along the cereal bowl and peered over the rim into the curve of an upside-down smile.

"New in the neighborhood?" I asked.

Kristen Skedgell

Misquamicut Beach, 2016

This is my ocean, these waves
hold me up like the palm of
a mother's hand like the hand
I never had, not of stone,

But water that lifts and gives
and returns me to myself.
I belong to it. It belongs to me.
I am not a thief.

Shakespeare's Niece: Reflections of a Writer's Daughter

> *Let me imagine, since facts are so hard to come by, what would have happened had Shakespeare had a wonderfully talented sister.*
>
> Virginia Woolf
> *A Room of One's Own*

From the first time I stroked the soft palm-worn cloth of my mother's Modern Library classics to the moment I opened her first published novel, I have wanted to write. I remember that moment as though it were this morning -the sound of the washing machine churning in the basement, Mom's footsteps on the stairs, plodding up and down with another basket of laundry and me ensconced on her grey office couch, partaking of the forbidden fruit.

Mom's office was slightly larger than a walk-in closet with a tattered maroon oriental rug on the floor and a worn corduroy couch beneath two windows that looked out onto our suburban street. The walls were covered with shelves of cloth-bound books whose spines were the muted colors of desert vegetation — brown, beige, slate, ocher, and sage.

I was in the fourth grade, ostensibly home with a sore throat. I knew I wasn't supposed to touch the shiny new books in the cardboard box next to Mom's desk. Oil from my fingerprints would mar the sky blue dustcovers. I wiped my palms on my pajama bottoms, took a deep breath and plunged in. As daughter of the author, I felt it was my duty to verify the spelling of her name and make sure the book jacket photograph did her justice. I had no idea I was touching fire.

I soon found myself immersed in the soft cushions of the old couch, flipping through the pages of Mom's first-ever published novel. I'm sure my mother didn't suspect I was in there and, unless she caught me pawing through her new book, she wouldn't care except to stand in the doorway of the office, laundry basket in her arms and say, "I thought you said you were sick." Then she'd wearily walk away, not waiting to hear my brilliantly rehearsed defense. My whole childhood was full of questions she never waited around to hear the answers to. She drifted through our house like tumbleweed on the prairie, a disquieted spirit.

But then came her Book. Like a magnificent baby, a holy infant. The Savior. Mom's Book. One day, no baby — only piles of upside-down papers strewn across her desk. Next day, she was whisked off to the radio station and returned home with a brand-new Panasonic cassette recorder and a box full of promotional materials.

In the middle of the book, I found a two-page conversation, a refreshing break in the long blocks of text. I started to read. A woman and a man were sitting on a bed enveloped in cigarette smoke and discussing their bosses, children and spouses when suddenly the man stuck his tongue in the woman's mouth and unzipped her dress. I dropped the book. Then I picked it up and reread the section several times.

I'd had my first French kiss a few weeks earlier on a Saturday afternoon in the back row of a darkened theater during the Beatles' first full-length feature film "Help." It was an apt title for the backdrop of my first grown-up kiss at age 10. I got a hickey, too — an ugly red blotch on the side of my neck which I tried unsuccessfully to conceal under powder and a white turtleneck. Mom noticed it and said, "Where'd you get that" as though it were something that had just arrived in the mail. She didn't wait around to hear the answer. She passed through the room with something else in her hands — a bag of groceries, a bucket of cleansers, a basket of folded laundry.

I continued to read but when the lady started lamenting her 40th birthday, I returned the book to its box. Since when did my mother know about French kissing and adultery? So this is what she'd been up to, all those months, tapping away behind closed doors. I gazed around the room at her bookshelves. Something was going on here. What else was hidden between those deceptively plain covers? It made me want to read every book. It made me want to write one myself.

When I was eleven, I told my mother my dream of being of becoming a writer. We were in the laundry room, folding clothes. She said nothing at first, just snapped a pair of wrinkled jeans and looked away, as though I'd just announced my intention of joining the Army. "OK," she said at last. "But don't study writing like I did. Study life. Don't waste your time getting a master's in English Lit. Do your own research. Get your own material. Then you'll really have something to write about."

I listened to my mother. Adolescence is rife with material, especially if one is fortunate enough to have impossibly liberal parents. By age thirteen, I had experimented with practically everything — sex, drugs, alcohol, protesting of every conceivable cause — and nothing fazed them. In the end, it was my mother's mind-bending equanimity that led me to embrace the source of my most fruitful research — a right-wing Bible cult.

In the summer of 1970, when I was 14, a renegade preacher from Ohio rode into our town on the back of a raspberry Harley-Davidson and harvested a bumper crop of disaffected Nietzsche-reading high school students for the Lord. The Doctor, as he preferred to be called, guaranteed anyone over age 12 the answers to life's most troubling questions or their money back. And it worked. After 36 hours of monotone audiotapes, who cared whether or not the world was created in six days?

The Doctor believed in burning things — bridges, ballast, books. He held some rather uncommon beliefs, which I discovered only after I dropped out of college and followed him to Emporia, Kansas, home of the original Wizard of Oz. Once a year, we hauled our boxes, which we mostly lived out of, to an abandoned campground and cast our intellectual ballast into a seething bonfire. One year, I hurled *The Feminine Mystique* with a vague recollection of the autographed copy on Mom's bookshelf. Only years later did I read my mother's name in the "Acknowledgements" of that classic feminist text. The Doctor said bra burners were possessed. He also said the Holocaust never happened and an invisible East Coast elite, which included my parents, was conspiring to take over the world.

When I was growing up, literature was our religion and the Bible was merely part of that canon. Books, all books, were sacred. They were the only legitimate refuges from the brutishness of everyday life. They rescued me from my father's alcoholism and my mother's aloofness. Mom's bookshelves were the closest things we had to an altar. Before I could pronounce the word "fascist," I was taught that book burning was one of the most heinous crimes on earth.

My mother's long literary silence between Book #1 and Book #2 might be attributed, in part, to the many hours she spent composing newsy letters peppered with philosophical diatribes designed to lure me away from the cult. Little of what Mom said in those letters stuck with me. In fact, I did everything I could to purge myself of her satanic influence. But one thing was constant and that was her admonition to me to write. Write stories. Write poems. Write her. She saved all my letters, even the ones in which I meticulously detailed her failure as a wife and mother. During those twelve years of separation, perhaps the most beguiling aspect of her letters was that they continued to come at all.

By the time my mother's second novel was published, I had left the group and moved back home. Whatever fascination I had with the Doctor and his "Aw, shucks" megalomania left me so battered inside and out that when Mom flew to Oregon to meet her second grandchild, she bought extra plane tickets and smuggled the three of us — a toddler, a newborn and myself — back East. One of the first things I did when I arrived home was to visit the local library. Mom was curious about the titles I brought back. She recognized some of them, including *The Battered Woman,* a groundbreaking study on domestic abuse. Mom edited that book.

So began my next phase of research...another fifteen years worth of depression, anger, confusion, grief. The losses seemed endless. I started therapy, returned to college, remarried, started a career, raised a family, wrote a memoir and so on. All this while, I burned inside with resentment for what every therapist traced to my mother's "emotional neglect." But when I understood my mother's passionate preoccupation with the written word, I was finally able to accept her most invaluable gift.

My love of words came from her, my love of books, of dreaming and sifting and sorting out phrases, of sitting at my desk with the door closed, with children sleeping and laundry piling up and piles of face-down papers growing larger every day and of knowing, even in moments of deep despair, that some day, this, too, might make a good story.

Being a writer's daughter isn't easy. Neither is being a writer's mother. We each have our material. Thanks to her, I know what to do with it.

The Beggar

Downpour in Kiev, pedestrians scatter.
I cling for shelter beneath a shivering birch.
Beggar boy runs at me, cup in hand,
falls at my feet, red soaked shadow
with a puppy in his coat.
He pleads for hrvinas contorted smile,
coal-smudged cheeks, penny eyes, tarnished
and dull with rage.
I hand him a few rubles and he flees into the storm
to the next tree, the next mark.

Now that he is gone, I would take him in my arms
with his sad black puppy, dry his face and wash his dirty hair,
fit him with new clothes, take him to lunch,
buy him a bright red toy. I would kneel at his feet and hold his hand
and the hand I held would be the hand of the child that is me and
the kneeling one would be the parent I never had.
And my tears would fall on the grimy sidewalks
and into the polluted streets, into the dying grass
and the receiving earth would soften
and everything would grow
so no one would ever have to beg
for anything.

The Rescue

The year my husband didn't give me a card on my birthday we talked about it, of course, like civilized grown-ups do, though that's hardly what I'd call myself, blubbering, weeping mess on my bed alone in the afternoon after I took the new dog out in the first light snow of the year. She's a waggy all-paws pitbull-shepherd blend, a "rescue" with a scar above her soulful eyes who was found on a North Carolina street at midnight, dodging headlights, barking at dump trucks. She was barely a year old and pregnant and somebody let her go, knocked up then thrown out on the street because nobody wanted you –they picked her up behind a dumpster and brought her to a shelter where she had eight puppies. Imagine a seven year girl and mother of eight.

When I was thirteen, I was raped by the boy down the street. Not so much a boy, he was draft age and I guess I let him or so I've always told myself because I didn't fight back, I mean, he was stronger, definitely stronger and our mothers belonged to the same Women's Consciousness Raising Group — they were friends — and I thought we were, too until he pushed me down, his hands on my forehead forcing me, his legs on my legs prying them open and I couldn't stop shivering. My teeth were chattering, my whole body shaking as though it had fallen into a sea of ice. I told my mother because I was afraid. I didn't want to be pregnant. I didn't want to be sent away.

My mother dismissed it with a wave of her hand and assured me that if I was indeed what I thought, though I probably wasn't, we would fly together to colorful island of Puerto Rico where I could get an abortion. In the meantime, she ran the water in the tub for a douche. She was a feminist, see, and she knew them all — Freidan, Abzug, Steinem — Mom wrote books, too, and deep down I think she was glad I was "normal" and sexually liberated like she had been in her Greenwich Village days — that I wasn't such a square sheltered suburban kid who babysat and liked it and loved horses and puppies. Because she sounded almost gleeful when she said that perhaps it was time for me to get fitted for a diaphragm now that I was "sexually active." Instead I joined a Christian cult.

On my first date with my husband, I tried to be as absolutely forthright and honest as I could be. We drank beer in a booth at the old smoky pool hall, which is now rated in Zagat's as the best old pub in the state, and I told I him what a mess I really was, inside that is, that I'd been in the psych ward not just once and lost my children and I was on Lithium and even though I was happy now I could disappear like someone thrown out into the driving rain, wind blowing you this way and that, nothing to hold onto, thunder so loud, you cover your ears like the Screaming Man and lightning threatening to strike and take away the past — like ECT. What was ECT? he asked.

He fell in love with me then, I guess. The good, honest, stupid, innocent part of me that was trying to warn him. Trying to throw up the flares that signaled danger. Danger! Enter at your own risk. I'm broken. I'm a rescue. But he didn't believe me. He married me anyway. All he saw then, he says now, was a vivacious, funny, intelligent and beautiful woman. Love is blind and he's living proof of it.

And now, on my birthday, after years and years of worsening depressions — depressions so bad he's scared to let me out of his sight, he panics at the thought of what to get me and how to tell me just exactly what he feels in a card. "It's been exhausting," he said. "Utterly exhausting." Unable to find a card that could untangle the aching knots inside him, that would say something like, "I hate you but I'm glad you were born. I wish I didn't love you so goddamned much, goddamnit." At least that would have been honest. But they don't make cards like that at Hallmark.

So, no card this year. No little pastel stickies hidden throughout the house in funny places either, on the shelf of the medicine cabinet, under my cell phone, inside the tissue box. Not even a picture like he used to draw or a funny little poem. I've sucked the inspiration right out of him. Wife of a world-class artist. I never wanted to be. I knew I would ruin it. I felt so so sorry for myself as I cried alone on our bed. Oh, what have I done to him? What have I done to this lovely man, the only one who ever loved me, who never mistreated me? And I cried even more, feeling sorry for him as well.

Around 5:00, he called to me from the downstairs. "Where did you go? I thought we were going to bake a cake." He trudged up to the bedroom and stopped in the doorway, "Oh," he said, "You've been crying again." He leaned against the frame, braced himself. I tried to speak in "I" statements. He listened like he always does but I could sense his fear. I don't remember the order of what happened next. Everything always speeds up at the end.

Winter sunlight burnt-sienna splashed on peach-painted walls. A large lit candle in a red-tinted jar. Carole King singing "Natural Woman" and several rounds of champagne with toasts and cheese doodles and the smell of Bay Rum and an apple tasting warming massage oil in a heart-shaped plastic bottle warm on my finger on his tongue then his wool robe which I rested my cheek on and I asked if it felt itchy and he said no. And there was fire in the mirror above my bureau, smoke billowing all around. Our room was ablaze like 42nd St. and the Sixties and Fred Astaire and Ginger Rogers tapping and swirling with laughter and song. And the setting sun glowed like a jack-o-lantern above our heads, those last radiant moments even brighter now because twilight had arrived.

Merima Trako

Srebrenica Genocide Memorial. Photo by Almas and Kanita Suljevic.

Life Interrupted

New Hampshire, United States of America
July 11th, 2015

Hamida sat by the window. Her small apartment was stuffy and the air outside was so heavy that she felt as if she was looking through a curtain of mist. She could see slow moving cars outside her two story apartment building. She rocked slowly, back and forth, back and forth. The smooth motion of her movement kept her mind quiet and calm. The chair was green, with purple flowers, base wooden. It was an old rocking chair she picked up at the flea market when she arrived in the United States in 1997. The news of yet another anniversary of Srebrenica was scarce and no one paid particular attention to the Russian sanctions in the UN Security Council. Hamida did not expect this to resonate through ether of the constant flashes of "You will not believe what she did next, click here to view" celebrity videos seeping through the social media and now even the news.

She rose slowly hugging her slim form and walked over to the bureau next to her full size bed. It was neatly made. The whole room was tidy, scarcely furnished. The bed, the rocking chair and the bureau were the only things occupying this hot, suffocating room. On the bureau she stroked the small wooden box with the writings from a paragraph of the *Qu'ran* her grandmother gave her. She kept her teenage girl prized possessions in this box when she left home. This was the only object besides an extra pair of underwear she took with her when the soldiers came to collect them. She lifted its cover after a few moments and took a couple of black and white photographs out; her mother, father, two brothers, and her as a baby in her mother's lap set on a 1970s-style sofa grinning at the camera. Second photograph showed her as a little girl and her brothers standing in their front yard. Their old white Fiat was visible in the background. She turned the photograph around, July 1983 it said in a neat, sloped cursive writing. She was five years old and she remembered this photograph being taken. Her uncle, who came from

Germany that year where he worked in construction, brought back a brand new Olympus that he was excited to show off in the village. In those days cameras were rare and photographs were cherished once developed. In the age of iPhones and digital cameras, where every moment is captured and little is left for the actual living, the photographs were no longer symbols of happiness and remembrance. They were witnesses of decay of human self absorption. Uncle Sakib had them line up so that he could snap a few photographs, to take the camera for a test drive. She also remembered a watermelon he brought and how the juice streaked down her chin and her bare legs. Her mother scolded her for staining her blouse, but she did so mildly, as she always did with all her children. Hamida was her youngest. Cherished by her father who called her "*Sine*" (My Son) even though he already had two sons. She liked being pulled onto his lap in the evenings when he sat on the bench in front of their house smoking cigarettes and waiting for the dusk to arrive after a long day working in the fields. He always had a gleam in his eye when he stroked her hair and talked softly about the work he had to do the next day. That was her "*babo*", a strong, utilitarian man. His callused hands stroked her cheek often and she felt the ridges on the finger tips, never harsh but always welcoming. His scent of sweat, grass, and sometimes the cow dung that stuck to his shoes, lingered in her nostrils, not unpleasant, but as a fond memory that comforted her.

Hamida was absorbed by her brothers' faces. They looked so much like her father: young, grinning, full of life. She stroked the picture and replaced it in the small box. She stood there for a moment and then returned to her chair. She picked up a book and set it back on her lap. She looked out the window once more and rocked back and forth. The book lay there in her lap. Hamida stayed in the chair not picking it up, the quiet was always her cloak, as the memories rushed through her. She could not escape them; her father's scream when they took her brothers; soldiers laughing and pushing him away; her mother clawing at the soldier's stained uniform; the soldier swinging his hand and backhanding her across the face, sending her sprawling on the doorstep where she stood; another soldier telling her to get up and take Hamida to join the other women standing on the road. Hamida replayed the moment when her mother got up and grabbed her hand. She replayed the last time she saw her father, when one of the soldiers grabbed his arms and pushed him behind the house where her brothers were dragged earlier. She blocked many other memories: walking to the gathering place where they were kept waiting for the buses to take them away, her mother's crying, the smell of despair that was everywhere.

Next morning Hamida woke up with a dull headache. This was a common occurrence after the night spent rolling around in her bed waiting for sleep to come. She got up and trudged to the small bathroom in the hallway of her condo. She showered and dressed briefly glancing at the box on the bureau. She left the apartment quietly and walked to her small beat up Dodge Neon. It worked, barely, and as she turned the key she sighed with relief that the car was willing to give her one more day. As she drove into the factory parking lot she prepared herself mentally for the day filled with invoices and collection issues. She worked in the accounting department of a small manufacturing company that produced medical instruments. The place was clean and organized. Her coworker, Lisa, was a quiet middle-aged woman who kept to herself. Hamida called good morning as she walked in and sat at her desk and booted up her computer. Opening her email she leaned over to leave her purse in the desk drawer. Glancing back at the screen one email caught her eye. The subject read: Long Lost Friend. The name in the TO field looked familiar, Samira Puric. Hamida gingerly opened the e-mail and began to read.

Dear Hamida,

I don't know if you remember me or if this is actually you. I got this email from your cousin, Sakib's son. He lives in Sweden in a town where I work. We were but girls in 1991 *when the war started and by* 1995 *when we last saw each other we both left Bosnia as young mature adults given the circumstances.*

I was at the funeral when your brothers and father were buried along with the other man found in the mass grave last year. It was the same as the funeral I went to the previous year, when they buried the remains of my father and my brother. I did not see you there. I suspect you could not come or you did not want to face the past that we both wish did not happen. I remember you and our time spent in the orchards on the outskirts our village sampling ripe apples from the fruit pregnant trees; the freedom with which we moved through the woods, through our village; long lazy days spent in the grass behind my house playing with the dolls that your uncle brought us from Germany. After that my memory becomes blurry and I am filled with anxiety whenever my thoughts bring me to those last four years of our lives in Srebrenica. I live every day pretending we did not exist in 1995 and today when the world is looking back to the moment in time when the part of me died I choose to remember you and our childhood. This transcends the hurt and the memories that claw at me every day. I am writing this letter to reach out to the soul who perhaps understands this turmoil and the agony and the desperation that I try to hide every day. If you are there and you receive my letter please do not stay silent. I hope that we did not lose each other like we lost everything else. Perhaps we can talk, email, message. God knows that nowadays there are ways. I have been silent for many years, and so have you. I am alone, as you are. I have heard of your mother's passing. Mine died on that bus. Bleeding could not be stopped. You remember. My aunt took care of me, but she had three children of her own. I live day to day, trapped in this mind and every day I look for an escape. I do not have the courage to do what my mind is telling me to do. I think of you and I hope you may have more strength than me. I don't know. So, my friend, write if this letter finds you. Write because this friend may be lost forever in the pool of darkness, stronger than the light that may exist out there. I, however, do not see it.

Your friend,

Samira

Hamida read and re-read the letter. She could see Samira. Her dirty blond hair and her clear blue eyes always full of mischief. She remembered the days they spent together and the ease with which they spent hours silently starring at the sky in the orchard comfortably relaxing , their bellies full of ripe apples, while the bees buzzed around them. Hamida got up and took her purse. Lisa looked at her puzzled.

" Where are you going?" she asked with a quiet voice, brows drawn together.

"I am leaving," said Hamida. Suddenly she felt an urge to run, run until she was free of this place.

"Leaving to go where?" Lisa completely abandoning her task and turning her chair to face Hamida.

" I am going to see an old friend." Hamida turned her computer off while she spoke. "She lives in Sweden."

"In Sweden?" Lisa's voice was rising. "I didn't know you were taking a vacation."

"I didn't know myself." said Hamida with a small smile. "I will let you know when I'm returning."

"But, don't you need to notify the HR? What will Mr. Smith say?" Lisa was walking now behind Hamida who was striding down the hallway.

"You can let him know and he can call me on my cell." Hamida was now rushing, wanting to get rid of Lisa.

At the entrance she turned and looked at the small mousy Lisa, her hair in a neat bun, her eyes, too small for her face sharply studying Hamida.

"It will be okay Lisa. It's not the end of the world. People take time off work; they live, heck, they die for no reason. I too, will die some day and perhaps even lose this job, but that's okay. The world moves on. We have but ourselves to believe in and perhaps others to save." Hamida spoke in a rush. She swung the door of the lobby open and stepped in the hot summer day leaving Lisa staring after her. She raised her face to the sky and smiled broadly for the first time in the past twenty years. She was going home.

Ignore

Ignore me.
I will ignore you.
Ignore the news.
Ignore the truths.
Ignore, be blind.
Hide.
Ignore.
No pride.
Just close your eyes.
No surprise.
No fondness.
Trust the lies.
Ignore the power.
Ignore the poor.
Hunger,
drought,
and summer,
and fall,
and winter,
and global warming,
and war.
Ignore,
mostly war,
and politics.
If you ignore
you will last,
otherwise
you are the past.

Us, Beyond the War

They lay on an old blanket they stole from Dado's parents. They were eighteen, free now to venture atop of the mountain that only a few short months ago housed killing machinery that regularly bombed the town. Nejra was quiet, her head on her hands, only close strands of grass in her frame of vision. She was picturing the long range missile guns as passive robots, ignoring the thoughts of the people who stood behind those triggers and fired the grenades that fell like rain on unassuming humans who were in search of water, or children who happened to be going to school thinking it might be safe that day. It was all disconnected and unreal today, by the water, listening to the voices of the other picnickers and the rush of the river's flow.

As they sat soaking the sun, their bones melting under the heat, their bodies limp and glued to the fabric underneath. River was just beyond the giant rocks bordering its bank, like a stone castle wall placed there by nature, keeping its beauty hidden and locked away from the unexpected onlookers. They knew that the river was there, the rustling sound of its movement mixed with the summer breeze and the buzz of the voices around them told them that it was real, lush, green, and alive. Other townsfolk have also escaped the punishing heat of the late summer that bounced off the brick buildings amplifying its force. They replaced the wave of the hot stifling air with the cool breeze of the mountain and the water's own cooling effect, cold current surrounding it while the rushing mass made its descent down the stony slopes to the valley below, untainted, fresh and mysterious.

Beyond the rocks that were washed away from the rough peaks at the mountain, the river had a natural swimming hole. Rocks tumbled when the earth shook with the violence of gods eons ago. Townspeople knew that the water was icy cold, yet, they went willingly and soaked their feet until their toes turned numb. Some swam and came out shivering, lips blue, running to the warm smooth rocks to dry and enjoy the momentary comfort of the cool skin in the warm air.

The sun was at its zenith and Dado squinted up at it, and then turned to look at the others. "Man, this shit is hot. I gotta go cool down."

It was a sign. Boys stood up and followed him down to the edge of the river. In a few minutes they were hidden by the impenetrable stone wall, as nature intended them to be. The river was free to swallow them and no one would ever know that the boys were there.

Sanja rose on her elbows gazing towards the river until she could see a faint trace of smoke circling the wall and escaping around the edges.

"They're smoking IT again," she said, not elaborating what, they all knew it was not the Drina cigarettes. That was too war-like. They were "free" now after all.

"Where did they get IT?" Maja asked

"Bajro probably. He's been getting it from Split."

"They won't be able to drive." Nejra spoke, her voice muffled as she lay face down, her head buried in her folded arms; her bare legs flashing white under her short-cropped jean shorts; her bare back protected only by a thin strap of a bikini top was turning red; no SPF protection. Sunscreen did not make it to the town's stores yet. People were more concerned about getting chocolate, cigarettes, sugar and flour to the empty shelves.

"Who cares. We can't go fast in that junk of a car anyway." Sanja said reaching for a beer.

They were quiet for some time watching, observing the crowd around them. Nejra turned her head to one side. She wanted to read their thoughts, to see what they lost in the past three years. What did they regret and how did they manage to forget the fears and struggles to be here, in the sun, by the river, for just a moment feeling normal, like the rest of the world? All of them were engrossed in their own conversations, some even laughed. Food started to resemble normal food (not canned crap they ate for months): sandwiches with real lunch meat, salami, cheese. It was heaven; beer from Sarajevo brewery and Drina cigarettes. It was all still very pricey but it was becoming more affordable by the day. Even "ganja" that came from Croatia now was affordable, no embargoes or expensive checkpoint pay-offs to cross the enemy lines.

A couple next to a big oak tree was making out. The man's assault of the tongue left little to everyone's imagination. They were young, Nejra could tell, slightly older than she, maybe early twenties.

"Get a room" she commented suddenly jumping up to stretch her hands over her head.

She walked towards the rocks. They were cool to the touch, smooth and soothing under her palms, this side was shaded from the sun. She leaned against them facing her back towards their hard surface. She watched the couple through her hooded eyes. Suddenly she realized that there was a little boy teetering around their blanket, leaning down every so often, picking flowers, and throwing them in the air. He tilted his head and as he walked he had a hard time keeping his balance. Nejra thought he was sick. She averted her eyes.

She looked up at the sky and she saw fluffy white clouds that were floating in the vast blue pool, endless and beautiful. She wondered who was up there. Was it God? Did He allow them this beauty now, just for a day, so that they could feel His mercy? Would He throw them back into the darkness, scorching their senses, forcing them to pray and trust that He would save them, perhaps throw in another day in the sun, soaking up the beauty of His nature, believing that He was, in fact, merciful. Nejra remembered her early childhood, days spent in the large city where she was born, under the shades of large linden trees. Her naïve, happy disposition was gone now, replaced by this suspicious, quiet and hardened girl/woman who was about to leave everything behind and travel to yet another unknown, to a future that was as unpredictable as the war that was now behind her.

Dado appeared behind the rock and glided towards her. The hazy look in his eyes told her that he smoked his share of the weed supply. He slung his arm around her shoulders and leaned against the rock next to her. He silently offered her a cigarette and she took it. Bending forward to catch the lighter's flame, she noticed the "making out couple" heading towards the car parked under the row of trees next to the road. Sex was back in fashion. God and religion that took the center stage during the disparity of the days without electricity and food and death and decay that used to be all around them, was now replaced by this corporeal pleasure activity. They were alive, they made it, they wanted to feel everything, sweetness of the cakes, cigarette smoke, cold, and the heat and orgasms, lots of orgasms.

She caught Dado looking at her out of the corner of her eye.

"What?" she asked.

"Jealous?" He smiled.

She laughed. "Of those two?" she gestured towards the couple. " Suuure," she drew out the word, feeling relaxed next to him, no pressure, no expectations, she could be whatever she wanted to be.

Dado laughed now too. His laugh was clean, loud and it rang through the air bouncing against the hard surfaces, so that the others who still lounged on the blanket looked up at them. He waved and lit his cigarette. They stood there, each waiting for the other to speak. Nejra did not feel pressured to say something. With Dado she could be quiet, ponder the situations, think about the couple having sex in the car without feeling ashamed or needing to kiss him or somehow respond to the sexuality that hung in the air.

"Did you get your tickets?" he asked, smoke surrounding his face, making him appear ghost like.

"No, not yet. The sponsors said they were sending them next week. I hope our post service doesn't screw things up. I doubt the plane tickets to Chicago are cheap, especially coming from Sarajevo." Nejra puffed the cigarette , enjoying the feeling of floating she got when she inhaled the strong Drina smoke.

"Are you scared?"

"I'm not really thinking about it. It can't be worse than the war," she smiled.

Everyone said that these days. Whatever happened, broken leg, hunger, "It can't be worse than the war." Everyone was just happy to have survived the nightmare, other stuff didn't matter. You could've thrown a natural disaster on the citizens of Bosnia and Herzegovina and they would've just shrugged, "Eh, it can't be worse than the war."

They continued to smoke. Nejra looked towards the river, a small sliver of sun's reflection off the water's edge peeked between the bushes and she saw the kid that was teetering around the blanket. Nejra suddenly realized what was so unusual about him. He reminded her of her father when he came home drunk. She looked and saw a discarded bottle of beer near the edge of the blanket. He tilted his body to the right, his eyes droopy, he flailed his hands trying to keep his balance as he fell sideways, getting up again, trying to walk. She had to look away. The site was grotesque and unsettling, heaviness of the image sat in her stomach. The cigarette did not taste so good anymore. A cloud floated over the yellow ball overhead and the feeling of loss moved through her, inexplicable. Dado noticed the kid, too. He did not say anything, just shook his head. He pulled her closer and they both pushed away from the stone walking towards their friends.

"Let's celebrate" Dado said. "Nejra is going on an adventure."

Other boys were now emerging from behind the rocks, Amir, Denis and Hare. They all had the same hazy look in their eyes. The kid bumped into Amir and went down in slow motion. Amir looked at him confused. They both seemed out of place in this moment. A miniature drunken version of the older boy, high on ganja. Nejra was mesmerized. She sat down and leaned on her hands watching the sky that was still blue, the sun was gone, covered by the white cloud, reflecting her thoughts.

Walls were being brought down. Air travel was possible, no more tunnel under the runway, carrying ammunition, people. Now, big mechanical birds were flying over the wounded land that kept its dark secrets and pain hidden in the mountains. One of these birds would take her away, she would be free. The kid would remain the prisoner. He did not know the war, but he would know the fallout and the harsh reality of after. There was no more faith left in people that things would be better. Everything would stop; times would carry the hate without the hope that there was something beyond the horror.

He Looks Like Kenan

10/19/15

He looks like my Kenan!
Thin black shirt
lifted on his bare back
as he lies in the sand
face down
arms by his side.
He is sleeping
like my Kenan.

His small, three year old leg
bent on one side
nestled in the sand
his face turned
towards the sun
in the sand
peaceful
free
while he is sleeping
like my Kenan.

Arms lifted him up
face of a soldier,
sadness and anger.
He is small,
he is three years old
and he is lying in the sand.

Sleeping
he must be sleeping,
he should be sleeping.
safe,
dreaming of cookies,
of sun and play,
and warmth of his mother's arms
like my Kenan
he must be sleeping.

He looks like my Kenan,
but
is he sleeping?
He is not smiling
in his sleep
like my long-lashed
bright-eyed
vivacious
happy
mischievous
Kenan.

He is buried,
lost,
unlucky to have been born,
to have lived in this dark hour
of human greed,
of human failure to be human
to act human
to abandon the animal inside.

He is lost in the sea
his departed soul
merged with the Universe
not God
showing the fragments of his sad boyhood.

He looks like my Kenan,
I am his mother
the pain tells me
I am his
and he is my Kenan
now gone
in the darkness of human hell.

Nancy Glover

A Brittle Peace

She has not fallen off the shelf of ice into the open water.

My mother's lying on her side with her back to the door, the sheet turned down over the top of the blanket and the bony hill of her shoulder like the flap of an envelope, the room deep charcoal, and lavender-blue shadows. I skid across the sheer ice between us and wait for her to emerge from the daze of half-awakeness.

"Oh, Nancy," she says.

She turns her back on the daily activities in which he tries to interest her. She's insistent. She wants the door halfway closed so she doesn't feel exposed, yet halfway open so she doesn't feel closed in.

Somewhere behind her eyelids is my mother. She's in there, brittle yet intractable. She will not give in. Neither will I.

I perch on the edge of the bed. She turns to me like a plant to sunlight.

"Your father's given up on me," she says, her eyes like still ponds, provocative.

"Well, I haven't," I tell her. She takes this in like medicine, testing the taste of it.

"You're kind," she says.

I go back to the living room, leaving the door halfway open, halfway closed.

"You see what I'm up against," my father says.

"Yes, I see."

I feel the precariousness of his need for reassurance. We sit without speaking, their classical music radio station playing in the middle ground. I feel the weight of her self-negation, the take-away game she has created.

In grade school, we made Christmas trees made out of green construction paper. We folded the paper in half, traced one side of the tree, cut along the outline, opened the paper and — a whole and perfect tree emerged. Then came the Elmer's glue and baby powder, which we applied. We were then told to hang them on the bulletin board along the classroom wall.

But I wanted one for my mother. I wanted to make her one of these trees. When I got home I searched for green construction paper. Finding none, I took a piece of plain white typing paper from a desk drawer and colored it with my green Crayola crayon. Elmer's from the laundry room closet, talcum powder from the canister on my dresser.

Somehow in the process of cleaning up, I lost it, this new-born tree, the glue still wet. I could hear her in their bedroom, the linen closet in the hallway between us. I crept quietly the short distance into the overhead glare.

"Mom?"

"What is it?"

"I made you a Christmas tree out of paper and glue and powder, but I can't find it. It disappeared, I don't know where it is." I was sobbing.

"YOU FIND THAT TREE," she said.

I knew she was imagining it stuck to the underside of a tablecloth or smudging her polished furniture.

How was I to produce something when I didn't know where it was?

Did I make another tree and show it to her, claiming I'd found it? I don't know. My memory tells me so. I wanted to make it okay.

I picture her on white hospital sheets, telling my dad to relay her love, but she will not take the phone and say it to me directly. I think of the prim, circular backhand in which she writes "With good wishes from mother and dad." Her words in the background sound muffled, as if coming from a snow cave. I want her to be okay, but hope is premature, my father says. If there's anything that gives her solace except for sleep, he hasn't found it, and the days slip by silent as snowfall.

When he talks to me, he names things that were always abstract or felt like the temperature of the moon. Because he has to. Because he's up against the white wall of her obstinacy, because he has depleted his resources. Because there is only me there with him at the round table under the rattan lampshade in the white-walled container of their retirement.

This is what they have come to. These three rooms. Four, counting the kitchen, which she doesn't, grateful that it isn't open to the living room because the sight and smell of food sends her scurrying to her room and the mahogany bed they received as a wedding present from his parents sixty years ago.

He arranges for me to have lunch in the resident dining room with Harry Stein who tells me about going to visit a well-known harpsichordist. After he knocked, she waited for him to open the door because she saved her hands for the keyboard.

Harry plays his own harpsichord less and less every day, but does not stop. He wants to know what's going on with my mother. He wants to hear the notes, not the hazy, shapeless tones my father offers. He wants to understand how the piece is constructed. He takes a packet of vitamins from his pocket, for macular degeneration, he says, so he will continue to be able to see his music.

"What does she do all day?" he asks.

I shrug.

"Old age is a chess game," he tells me. "It makes a move and you try to outwit it."

But she has not made her move. Maybe she thinks she has to wait for someone — doctors perhaps — to tell her what to do. Perhaps she's afraid that if she gets well and has to start going down to the dining room again, she'll feel naked.

When I get back upstairs to the apartment, she's lying on her side on top of the spread of the newly-made bed. She has demanded this, that it be made right.

"There's only one right way to make a bed," she says.

"Who are you, Martha Stewart?" I ask.

She doesn't respond but looks incredulous that anyone wouldn't know.

The woman who came to clean yesterday didn't know. She normally worked in the laundry. She told me that she hadn't made a bed with an electric blanket before. She hoped she'd done it right. Even my father and I together had had trouble lifting up the end of the mattress while grappling for the plug in the practically non-existent crevice between the mattress and footboard.

But my mother isn't satisfied. The white fringes of the spread are visible beneath the footboard and the top sheet isn't turned down far enough over the blanket.

Since October, his universe has imploded to the size of their apartment. He hasn't been down to the resident dining room. He's had trays delivered from the kitchen. When the tray arrives, my mother scurries off to the bedroom, saying, "The smell of food makes me nauseous."

I follow her into the bedroom to get her settled.

"Your father hates to eat alone," she says.

Since I arrived, he has ordered a tray for me as well. I can hear him in the kitchen, transferring the food from the Styrofoam tray and plastic containers to their Franciscan bamboo-patterned dinner plates he's warmed in the oven.

After the meal, he holds up the cookie he's eating. "Look," he says, "you can see the universe."

Sure enough. When I bend down next to him and look up at the thin, round ginger snap against the overhead light, it's stamped with tiny holes, that could, indeed, be seen as points of light in a night sky.

When we're finished, he makes a beeline for his wing chair in the living room and falls asleep. In the kitchen, surveying the detritus of the meal, I sense the enormity of his Everest. He can't get her to eat, he can't go down to the dining room because that may be the moment she lets down her resistance and wants a Saltine.

Later, the food safely out of range, she emerges in her flannel nightgown and my father's blue and white striped seersucker bathrobe.

"Will you come and be with me?" she asks him as he tips forward in the wing chair. He transplants himself a few feet to the end of the couch, and she nestles in with her back against his side, her knees like tent poles inside the robe. An old Fred Astaire/Ginger Rogers film comes on the tv. He places his arm over her shoulder. "You're all sweaty," he says with such tenderness that I think of the photograph he took of her in their first apartment, standing next to the Freed-Eisemann he'd gotten with his second paycheck, lowering an LP onto the turntable, smiling in a way that said I've gotten what I wanted.

Later, when I ask him what it is she wants, what might make her want to get well, he says, "She wants to be with me."

On the kitchen counter, a black three-ring binder, the compendium of pharmaceuticals that sustain them. It used to contain his alone — Coumaden and other necessities of post-heart-bypass surgery. It now contains a section for her, as well — pain killers for the compression fractures in her spine, sleeping pills, vitamins, calcium, anti-nausea, anti-diarrheal, anti-constipatory, anti-gas, antidepressants, and a collection of information sheets accompanied by drawings of each pill he's done with a drafting template.

A metal 4x6 file box containing his plastic jars of pills, each marked with a green or red or half-green, half-red dot for morning only, morning and evening, with or without food. Next to this, a shoe box with blister cards of medications she was given when she was in the health care center.

His routine isn't new. He's been at it for ten years. Adding hers has complicated matters to the point of distraction. "I forgot to take my meds this morning," he tells me, visibly shaken.

Mornings, he prepares tea and toast for her and shuttles it to the table on the seat of his walker. "I told her I won't be able to do this indefinitely," he says.

Although my father and I and the Loebs have been seated in the far corner of the communal dining room, I have trouble hearing Alice Loeb over the din of what sounds like fifty bridge parties. Her husband engages my father in the details about the satellite dish he had constructed on his former property to receive Russian television.

Alice has a bird-like quality about her. She keeps turning toward me as if to speak, but then doesn't. Finally she says, "Tell me, what's going on with your mother?"

Again I find myself a conduit for her unexplained absence. I wonder if Alice feels her own impending extinction as I explain about the compression fractures, osteoporosis, diverticulitis, tinnitus, lack of appetite, depression.

"I know what it's like," she says, telling me about how upended she'd felt when she had moved here. "It's harder for a woman."

Meanwhile, her husband disappears and returns with a folder with several 8x10 photographs, screen shots of Moscow television, which he gives me to take back to show to my mother. He thinks she might be interested. It feels like his contribution.

The apartment reeks of stagnation when we get back, of unopened windows and heat running full throttle.

"Things don't smell fresh to me anymore," my mother says, as if something has changed in the laundry detergent. "Is it me?"

I can't answer, yes, it is you, lying in bed without showering. It feels irreverent.

My father takes the direct approach. "I want you to get up and shower."

She looks at me with the look of a condemned prisoner. "We had someone come to help me, but it wasn't what I expected. I stood there on the mat while they gave me a sponge bath. I felt all soapy afterwards."

"So that's not what you want?" I ask. "You want to get in the shower?"

"Yes, but I'm afraid if I bend over to do my legs, I'll get dizzy."

"So why don't you call me when you're ready, and I'll do your legs?"

"How will I get dry?"

"I'll help you."

So we negotiate, we bargain, we deconstruct the process until she's satisfied. I lie on the bed, listening to the sound of the water the way I used to as a child, the comfort of it on the other side of the wall next to my bed. I wait for her to call to tell me she's ready.

There's no precedent for this. I have no training for this contingency. There's no instruction book. But here we are, standing facing one another, her skin lose and ill-fitting, her ribs prominent as cheekbones.

I tell her it reminds me of the beach, how she used to wrap my towel around me when I came out of the lake. She tells me how I took my bathing suit off in the public shower at the ocean when I was two, because I thought that's what I was supposed to do. But standing here now, I'm not sure what I'm supposed to do.

"Please," he says to me, indicating a plastic grocery store bag of trash. "Could you take this down the hall to the room across the bridge? It's at the intersection of the hallway just before where the sitting area is on the right; there's a room marked 'trash'. See if you can see Venus when you come back over the bridge."

He says this with the concern reserved for a sick person, with regret for not being up to seeing it himself. I become a star-spotter by proxy. A surrogate. I'm not sure my credentials are in order.

I find the room marked 'trash' and send the plastic bag down the chute. Given the small size of the opening, I presume that the residents are not expected to have much trash, that trash-making must be an activity that declines with age, that everything possible has already been disposed of.

I return with the reassurance that all is well with the heavens, and for a brief moment he and I are standing at the living room window of our ranch house on Sunset Trail and he is pointing out a bright spot of light he calls Venus through the leafless branches of the pin oak.

He has been tracking daily sunrise/sunset data from the U.S. Naval Observatory on my cast-off laptop. Sunrise, sunset, dusk, civil twilight, along with the dew point, wind chill factor, prevailing winds and what's on the menu for dinner.

He's noted some discrepancies in the official sunrise/sunset times and has been collecting data to support his theory.

"Did I send you a copy of the photograph of the moon I took on the balcony?" he asks.

I nod, knowing what's to follow.

"I took it with that inexpensive thousand millimeter lens from Ritz Camera," he says, which I already knew because he had written the lens information beneath the image along with the speed and brand of the film.

The copy of *Gallileo's Daughter* I bought him sits on the top shelf of the bookshelves next to *A Brief History of Time*, which I thought he would also like. But he hasn't mentioned having read them and I don't want to ask or he will give them back.

I dream he and I are standing on the beach at sunset. Everyone has gone home. The lifeguard tower sits empty, the lake calm without the wake of powerboats. At their moorings, the hulls sway quietly, the dock rises and falls, a halyard taps against a mast, the last rays of sunset fade behind Knollcrest.

He turns to me and says — what? I can't make it out. My mother's not with us.

He's talking to me now as if there's no one there next to him, as if I'm invisible. He says that she had been depressed since soon after they were married. He tells me that she's talking about things from their past to the doctors and nurses in the hospital. "They happened so long ago. I can't see the good of bringing them up again," he says.

Things she's mentioned to me, how she quit her accounting job soon after their wedding. The apartment close to the locomotive factory that filled with soot. The move away from their families to the small ranch house and my father taking their one car to work. The first child, who didn't live, the second child, who "didn't grow" and died only two weeks before my own birth.

I nod at my father, recalling the day she told me about the other children. She'd finished vacuuming and put the vacuum cleaner away. She sat in the wing chair and I on the ottoman by the front window. "You're not to tell anyone," she said. The joy I felt that I had not been meant to be an only child, that I had had brothers! This knowledge that I was not allowed to share with anyone. I asked hopefully, "Will there be any more children?" She said, "No, I told your father I didn't think we should have any more."

I recall a summer evening, me sweating in my bed, the sound of her crying in their room.

"What's wrong?" I wanted to know.

"Nothing," he told me, "Go back to bed."

The next morning she was at the kitchen table, rouge, powder, lipstick, and eyebrows penciled in. (She needed them darkened for definition, she'd told me.)

I recall a time when she went to the hospital. My father had taken me to the Old Oak for pizza. "Don't tell your Mother," he'd said. Why was she in the hospital? I didn't know then and I don't know if he can talk about it now. I don't want risk this brittle peace between us.

If a photograph of me in her arms as a baby exists, I've never seen it. The old moon with the new moon in her arms, as the old poem goes. There is one picture with the three of us on the couch soon after my birth. She's leaning to one side, away from the epicenter, while he holds me up to the camera like a package, bemused.

There's something endearing about the simplicity of this visit. Past visits had been orchestrated in advance. He'd made reservations at a restaurant that came with a solid recommendation, down-loaded the menu and wine list, researched the wines, planned two alternative driving routes and the best prices on gas, and, of course, would I mind driving?

Now he's marooned between two alternatives that can be sent up from the kitchen. Since he's given up alcohol as "a scientific experiment," he's less rambunctious, less prone to hyperbole, somewhat subdued.

He tells me that full moons don't make good photographs. Part of it has to be hidden to make it interesting. Something to do with the proportions of darkness and light. I picture him out on their balcony with his thousand millimeter lens bringing down the moon to within arms' length, the cold December moon, while my mother hibernates under the covers.

She had wanted to open the boxes, the memorabilia, the postcards, everything she'd collected, and look at them together. But he didn't want to, she told me. He would rather photograph the moon.

She tells me about how after college she wanted to go to New York City and become an artist, but her parents talked her out of it. "They knew I didn't have enough talent. They didn't mean any harm. They were trying to protect me."

We were in Talbots and she was pointing out the fashion drawings on display and saying, "This is what I thought I would be doing."

"You have to honor your self," I tell her.

"You sound like Judith Ryan," she tells me, and I'm back in the studio on Springville Road with the waif-like woman in sky-blue tunic leading the half-dozen fifty-somethings and me through yoga poses. For an hour a week that summer, my mother and I did this together, along with a photographer married to a famous playwright and other local artistic women. Between pranayamas, I breathed in a sense of possibility and fulfillment.

We were lithe and limber, our bodies light as rice paper, our teacher's voice, flute music. We intersected with gravity at all angles, became weightless and abstract. The scale of our bodies tipped and reset.

If I rub this memory between my fingers like a talisman, I can conjure us as we were then.

My mother now blinks at me now from the bed, her eyes milky as the insides of oyster shells.

She may, in fact, get better. Who knows? I could wake tomorrow to see that they've found their footing and are again in the two-step so familiar to me, where I'm superfluous, a tiny bag of sand marked "daughter."

Robley Whitson

Cave Shaman

Zigzagging through living rock
deep within the cracked hide
that holds the earth together,
in those inmost cavern shrines,
it is always that lightless moment
just before the universe.

Even when we came in awe
with sharpened horn points
and ground grit pigments
to line and color sacred images
scratched into stone rituals,
our lamps were dark fire
freed from the light,
flickering shadows to dance with us.

I breathed in the smoky lamp
and breathed out the images of power
I pushed into the wall,
flaking off bits of stone
with the tip of a horn
while singing magic words
where water-dripping was the only sound.

You will never see inside my shapes,
you will never hear my echo in your bones,
unless there is dark fire-smoke in you
and you can push your way
into the hard surfaces
of the stuff of the earth –

then you will be the lines,
you will flush with the colors,
and become what I breathed.

Feel your way inside that Ibex
carved to be snared in the trap
of graved lines bent into springy staves
knotted together with the rawhide thongs.
Her dot of an eye cannot spot my cunning.
She lives high above the last trees
on the crag faces of the mountains,
so I carved no hooves for her-
she cannot dart away from my grasp.

If you really are inside the wall
then feel the heat of those three lines
that blend within the she-goat:
the woman beneath the animal belly
her form melting into the Ibex.
A center line for the swell of buttocks,
one long curve for flank and thigh,
another line for the other leg.
I carved no feet for the magic Huntress-
she must not escape my spell.

Bios

Alice Barstow

Alice Barstow has had a handful of careers and pursuits over the years with writing being a constant friend throughout all journeys, and the place that always feels the most at home. She resides in Connecticut, mothering two fascinating daughters, an overly excitable dog and moody cat, alongside her nurturing, and thankfully, very patient husband.

C. E. Wyllie

C. E. Wyllie is an archaeologist and natural science illustrator specializing in the iconography and hieroglyphic inscriptions of ancient Veracruz, Mexico. She taught rock climbing and ski-mountaineering for Outward Bound before earning a Ph.D in Anthropology from Yale University. She was an Associate Professor of Art History and Archaeology at the University of Hartford, and currently divides her time between northwestern Connecticut and New York City.

Davyne Verstandig

Davyne Verstandig is a lecturer in English and Creative Writing at University of Connecticut and Coordinator of the Writers Project. Her poetry books: *Pieces of the Whole* and *Provisions*. Her work appears in: *Sex and Sexuality in a Feminist World; Songs of the Marrow Bone;* and *Where Beach Meets Ocean*. She performed improvisational work, painting and poetry at The Knitting Factory and Housing Works Café in NYC, and has given readings throughout New England. She gives writing workshops yearly at Wisdom House Retreat and Conference Center in Litchfield, CT. She is a Justice of the Peace and Poet Laureate of Washington, CT. www.davyneverstandig.com.

Dimitri Rimsky

Dimitri Rimsky grew up in Washington, CT, where he continues to reside. He is a graduate of Shepaug Valley High School, class of 1965. He has been a talent agent, mime and graphic designer. He currently is a house painter, sometimes web designer and occasional poet. Dimitri has been performing his poetry at various coffee houses and other venues since he was 18 years old. Most recently he has read at the Washington Art Association, the Gunn Library, the Sherman Playhouse, and the Hidden Valley Eatery. A selected poem was published in the *Confluencia in the Valley* collected works, 2013.

Emelie Samuelson

Emelie Samuelson is a bookseller, reader, writer, and coffee addict. She loves animals and all things strange. Her main goal in life is to spread joy. She lives in Connecticut with her person and her dog.

Fee de Merell

Fee de Merell grew up in a post-industrial town in England. She dreamed of making a living as a writer, but instead became a financial auditor, at which point she decided to change her life and run away to America. She now lives in a post-industrial town in Connecticut and still doesn't make a living as a writer.

Jane Darby

Jane Darby has been a teacher and writer for decades. Currently she teaches six-year-olds at a lovely independent school in Washington Depot, Connecticut and writes as often as possible. Her articles, essays and short stories have appeared in various publications including *Lynx Eye, Washington Square Review, Storyglossia,* and *New York Runner Magazine.* She is working on a novel.

Joe Connolly

Joe Connolly lives in Middlebury with his wife Paula and three wonderful daughters. His writing reflects his experiences and interests combining athletics and spirituality. He is a four time Ironman Triathlete, Crossfit athlete, avid skier, and barely average golfer. He grew up Irish Catholic and currently blends his traditional upbringing with a curious exploration of Eastern faith and spiritual traditions. He works as a healthcare marketing executive with Trinity Health-New England in Hartford.

Karen LaFleur

Karen LaFleur is a digital artist, writer and animator. She merges elements of the graphic novel, picture book and animation into verbal/visual narratives that speak to the resiliency of the human heart to survive in ever-shifting landscapes. Her artworks exhibit nationally including at the Renwick Gallery of the Smithsonian Institution, the Cape Cod Museum of Fine Art, and Union Square in San Francisco. They can also be found in collections worldwide. www.lafleurartworks.com.

Kristen Skedgell

Kristen Skedgell grew up a tomboy, the daughter of an intellectual mother and a composer father. A graduate of Columbia university school of Social Work and Yale Divinity School, she has found writing to be her greatest ally in making sense of the world around and within her. She has two grown children and is partners with poet Afaa Michael Weaver. Her narrative non-fiction pieces have appeared in local and national publications and she is the author of *Losing the Way: A Memoir of Spiritual Longing, Manipulation, Abuse and Escape.* (Bay Tree Publication 2008)

Merima Trako

Merima was born and raised in Bosnia-Herzegovina (former Yugoslavia). A sudden nationalistic divide in the early nineties led to a bloody war where a third of the Bosnian population (mainly Muslims) were killed. Merima and her family escaped ethnic cleansing in Banjaluka (where she was born) and settled in Travnik where they stayed until the Dayton peace agreement was signed.

Her passion for writing started in high school and has continued throughout her life. She moved to the U.S. in 1999 to study engineering and mathematics, her other love. She now lives in Connecticut, is married and has two boys. As a woman, mother, refugee, and engineer, Merima is passionate about world issues and strives to speak about social injustices as seen from her multiple perspectives.

Nancy Glover

Nancy Glover has a background in newspaper reporting, photography and public relations. She moved to Connecticut seven years ago to be near her mother who was widowed and transitioning to assisted living. Since her passing she has been exploring writing memory pieces, landscape painting and dance and has been a chapbook contest finalist.

Robley Whitson

Robley Edward Whitson is Distinguished Professor of Theological Anthropology. After graduate study at Fordham and Yale Universities he was elected Doctoral Fellow in anthropology of religion. Later he was Chair of the Fordham University Theology Department, a Visiting Scholar at Princeton Theological Seminary, Advisory Board member for the Princeton World Religions Project, Professor of Theology and Anthropology of The Hartford Seminary. His books include *The Coming Convergence of World Religions*; *The Shakers: Two Centuries of Spiritual Reflection, Mysticism and Ecumenism; Mytholog: Poem, Poeming Elusion;* and others. His poems are also in *Songs of the Marrow Bone.*